Starve Cancer - Feed Your Dog!

A Nutrition Regimen for the Prevention and Treatment of Cancer in Dogs

Jo Cowden, PhD

and

Connie McMillan, DVM

Dogwise Publishing

Wenatchee, Washington U.S.A.

Starve Cancer - Feed Your Dog!
A Nutrition Regimen for the Prevention and Treatment of Cancer in Dogs

Jo Cowden, PhD and Connie McMillan, DVM

Dogwise Publishing
A Division of Direct Book Service, Inc.
403 South Mission Street, Wenatchee, Washington 98801
1-509-663-9115, 1-800-776-2665
www.dogwisepublishing.com / info@dogwisepublishing.com

© 2021 Jo Cowden, PhD and Connie McMillan, DVM

Art director: Jon Luke
Interior: Lindsay Davisson
Cover design: Jesús Cordero

Library of Congress Cataloging-in-Publication Data
Names: Cowden, Jo E., author. | McMillan, Connie, 1967- author.
Title: Starve cancer - feed your dog! : a nutrition regimen for the
    prevention and treatment of cancer in dogs / Jo Ellen Cowden, PhD and
    Connie McMillan, DVM.
Description: Wenatchee, Washington : Dogwise Publishing, [2021] | Includes
    bibliographical references and index.
Identifiers: LCCN 2021039225 | ISBN 9781617813108 (paperback)
Subjects: LCSH: Dogs--Diseases--Nutritional aspects. |
    Dogs--Diseases--Alternative treatment. | Dogs--Nutrition. | Veterinary
    oncology. | Cancer in animals.
Classification: LCC SF992.C35 C69 2021 | DDC 636.7/0896994--dc23
LC record available at https://lccn.loc.gov/2021039225

ISBN: 9781617813108   Printed in the U.S.A.

Not everything that is faced can be changed. But nothing can be changed until it is faced.

James Baldwin
(1924-1987)

In Memory

*This book is dedicated to Addie Kara, my American Eskimo and
rescue dog. She was my companion and best friend. She responded to
chemotherapy and never lost weight or became ill for a single day. I give
full credit to her detailed nutritional program for the quality of her life
during chemotherapy treatments. Addie Kara remained active during
treatment and loved long walks with me.*

~ JEC

Table of Contents

Foreword

The day has come. You feel scared, anxious, and rife with anticipation over what will be said at your visit. You are a pet owner, and your best friend has been diagnosed with cancer. You are about to meet with a veterinary oncologist who will examine your pet and provide information about what therapy is available, the efficacy of the therapy, how long you might have, and how this diagnosis and treatment for your pet will change both of your lives and routines. I am one of the veterinary oncologists on the other side of this conversation.

I met Dr. Cowden several years ago at an appointment just like this with her best friend, Addie Kara. A sweet, lively, and beautiful fluffy, white American Eskimo dog, Addie Kara had unfortunately been diagnosed with lymphoma, a common type of cancer to affect dogs. Although lymphoma is treatable with chemotherapy and steroids, it is not a cancer we typically expect to cure. Like most pet owners, Dr. Cowden wanted to know what more she could do, leading to a discussion on supplements and nutrition.

Nutrition is a sensitive and sometimes controversial subject in veterinary medicine, and some people can have as strong an opinion on nutrition as politics. As an oncologist, I want to make recommendations based on published data and science, of which there is little in the field of nutrition for veterinary oncology. Despite this, during my training as a student, intern, and then resident, I developed a special interest in nutrition for dogs. There are many ways to "feed the body" to maintain health, decrease inflammation, and naturally promote healing for several conditions. For some chronic diseases, such as chronic kidney disease, nutrition is the main source of therapy! Unfortunately, for cancer, there is less data. Cancer is also diverse, with highly variable outcomes depending on cancer type and treatment modality chosen. With few publications showing proven benefits, I often felt I could not make strong recommendations about dietary therapy for my cancer patients.

Fortunately, Dr. Cowden has compiled a comprehensive book of what is known. She has reviewed books and peer-reviewed articles on cancer nutrition in pets to create a how-to guide and provide information all in one place. She did this for you, having been in your shoes. No more scouring the internet, uncertain if the recommendations are trustworthy, and feeling overwhelmed by conflicting opinions. Think of the following book as a resource, providing you with everything you need to know about nutrition for your pet with cancer.

When it comes to cancer, it always feels like we can be doing more. If you are looking to do more than traditional therapy and feel strongly about implementing diet changes for your pet, this book can be your guide. The nutrition regimen it offers provides a specific plan of integrating diet, feeding, and weight management. Based on science, it can be used by both pet owners and veterinarians who want to recommend a diet to optimize health and quality of life.

This book is also guided and backed by another veterinarian, Dr. Connie McMillan. Dr. McMillan was Addie Kara's primary veterinarian, who first diagnosed her with lymphoma and referred her for an oncology consultation. I consider her a trusted colleague and referral partner. Together with Dr. McMillan, Dr. Cowden has created a practical approach to feeding your dog the right foods to fight cancer. Their nutrition regimen, based on *The Cancer Diet* (Ogilvie, 2000), provides clear, concise, and easy-to-follow advice on creating a well-balanced diet for your dog. Menus and meal planning are also included, as well as the encouragement to have fun and confidence when cooking for your pet!

I practice by giving people information and options. I want to help people make informed decisions, for themselves. I do not like telling people what to do. I may never recommend a specific diet to a client. However, my hope is that this book will help you feel that whatever diet you decide to feed your dog, you have the best information available. I hope if you do use this book, you can feel confident in your choice, and that however you decide to treat your dog, or feed your dog, you know that you are doing your best. Your dog knows you are doing your best. Your dog knows they are loved.

Sarah E. Lyles, DVM, DACVIM (Oncology)

Chapter 1
An Introduction

If you have selected this book to read, your dog was probably recently diagnosed with cancer. You may or may not understand what this diagnosis actually means and what you must do to help your dog. After all, your dog is your best friend, companion, and a member of your family. You were likely informed that it is critical that you take your dog to a veterinary oncologist. You may be in shock if your dog seems completely healthy. This cannot be happening, but you know that you must make decisions quickly. The panic, fear, and sadness you feel are indescribable. It is devastating for you when your veterinarian tells you that your dog has cancer. But it may be treatable if caught in the early stages of cancer.

It is important to completely understand the alternatives for care. Maybe sharing the news with someone close to you can help with making a decision. Your veterinarian can also help with your decision about cancer treatments. Many sources provide needed information; however, the accuracy of those sources is an important consideration. Convincingly hopeful stories from other pet owners may not be realistic or truthful. Remember, your dog is your best friend, so take time to gather the appropriate information. With all cancer management, the one thing you can do is to provide your dog with the best nutrition for longevity.

Cancer is aggressive, but successful treatments can include surgery, radiation and chemotherapy for localized tumors. Some cancers, such as lymphoma, are only treatable with chemotherapy. All can be successful, adding months and perhaps years to dogs' lives. The thought of chemotherapy for your dog may be terrifying; however, you have probably been assured that most dogs might maintain a good quality of life and have an increased survival time. But even so, the thought of your dog perhaps only having a few months to live can leave many dog owners with an indescribable feeling of fear, pain, and dread. The level of urgency to act must be considered very high!

Dr. Lyles—an oncology veterinarian—diagnosed Addie with stage IV lymphoma with survival time of one to two months if left untreated. We started chemotherapy immediately. Addie went into remission quickly and there were no side effects. We also discussed how the benefits of proper nutrition could benefit her treatment. With that in mind, I began research on cancer and nutrition in dogs. From my research, I learned that her nutrition program would be very important and could help strengthen her **immune system**. I had to help her every day and, in every way, possible. Her health and treatment became my life. Addie lived over a year after treatment was initiated. However, we did not achieve a second remission. Despite this, Addie never knew she was sick. I set a goal to complete the book before I lost my Addie Kara to cancer. That did not happen. I stopped writing for some time.

I recently returned to my writing, focused on current science-based research in nutrition for dogs with cancer. Only a few new publications were available for the dog owner. There was not a how-to guide on nutrition for dogs with cancer. I knew the emotions so many pet owners were experiencing. It was time to finish my book—Addie's book—for pet owners wanting to provide the right and best nutritional meals possible for their dog.

As a retired research professor, I knew how to perform in-depth literature searches for specific information. Published research articles on this topic were limited; however, there were a few good sources that had excellent references. I reviewed all the books that I could find that presented information about nutrition for dogs with cancer. Most were poorly documented and only provided a few new suggestions for nutrition for dogs with cancer. Even books written by vets tended to recommend diets based on experiences or anecdotal evidence rather than scientific documentation.

It was very clear that a how-to guide—based on science—was needed, because most pet owners (and many veterinarians) are not going to be skilled in performing literature searches. At a time of crisis, scanning the internet searching for answers to find the best nutrition program and experimenting with diets is likely not be in the best interest of their dogs.

Purpose of the book

This book is written for those who are experiencing the same bad news that I received and desperately want a "blueprint" for the best nutrition possible for their beloved dog. This book is a guide—a nutrition **regimen**—for you and your dog.

Our book details the importance of the nutrition program for dogs with cancer. The regimen is based on extensive science-based research by Gregory Ogilvie spanning a decade from 1995 to 2006. He first established "A Cancer Diet" for dogs with cancer in 1998, and his research was highlighted on CBS News special, *New Hope for Pet Cancer Victims.*

The purpose is threefold:

1. To present a Nutrition Regimen as a systematic plan including processes, steps, diets and menus which, when combined establish, a **Standard of Nutritional Intervention** for use by dog owners and veterinarians treating cancer in dogs.

2. To provide detailed information on the necessary ingredients for healthy intervention.

3. To provide the detailed structure of the nutritional regimen that we recommend.

A medical regimen is defined (Merriam Webster & Cambridge, 2020) as a prescribed course of treatment designed to improve, maintain, and preserve health. A nutrition regimen (NR) is a specific diet plan which includes structured treatment and a diet plan designed for the restoration of health. It is a highly referenced, multidisciplinary body of knowledge for those specializing in programs of veterinary medicine and dog owners who may benefit from detailed nutritional interventions for helping control cancer.

There is a strong emphasis in the book on providing accurate information for owners of millions of dogs diagnosed with cancer annually. Realizing that an individual's knowledge in nutrition will vary greatly, the book is written from a broad perspective. This NR expands Ogilvie's cancer diet (2000), including new ingredients that are vital for the therapeutic program of dogs with cancer. Chapters in the book will detail the benefits of omega-3 fish oil (the cornerstone of the diet), selenium, arginine, and glutamine in the diet of dogs with cancer. Foods containing these ingredients for a prepared diet are included in the **nutrition regimen menu**. The dog owner along with her veterinarian will be able to access this guide to make informed decisions about the most important and critical components of the dog's diet. Together you can select ingredients from the NR diet which have natural cancer-fighting qualities, contain antioxidants, reduce inflammation, slow the growth of cancer, decrease the side effects of chemotherapy, boost the immune system, and improve the quality of life for a dog with cancer.

The book offers a practical approach, providing easily understood alternatives for the best care pet owners can more easily give their beloved companions during a time of intense difficulty. It is intended as an accurate source of information to complement veterinary medicine and oncology recommendations for treatment. Even though research is limited, professionals are realizing that changes in the nutrition for dogs with cancer are beneficial to the quality of life during treatment.

Knowledge is power

A critical aspect of the book is encouragement of positive attitudes and self-confidence for pet owners and a realization that power comes with increased knowledge. Dog owners will be confident about the importance of nutrition for their pets during treatment. It is a hope-inspired book for dog owners, so that they can help their dog through treatment, optimizing their health and quality of life. Pet owners must learn everything they can to make informed decisions. Every day they may be faced with unpredicted challenges. They must have options and keep a balanced approach, as they become the "fighter" for their companions. The book stresses that dog owners must take charge of the pet's nutritional plan. It is important, and helpful, to remember that your dog does not know about cancer.

Maintaining a good appetite and controlling body weight

The emphasis in this book is on maintaining a good appetite and controlling the body weight of a dog diagnosed with cancer. Many factors impact the nutritional status of dogs with cancer. Before

cachexia—wasting away of lean body mass—causes the dog to lose strength, planned nutrition must be established. Increasing the amounts of food is not always the correct change in the diet.

A pioneering study more than 50 years ago (Harper, 1958) introduced the concept of creating an "imbalance" of amino acids (the building blocks of **protein**) to slow the growth of cancer cells. Cancer cells rely on certain amino acids for growth. The idea of overloading cancer cells with amino acids they do not want, and starving them of those that they want, sets the foundation for a therapeutic approach for cancer treatment. The study gave rise to the concept of dispensable and indispensable amino acids, clearly indicating the nutritive value of a protein was related to its amino acid composition. Our book is based on the concept of creating an imbalance of amino acids. Dogs with cancer must be fed a very different diet so they have the essential nutritional requirements to "fight" cancer, enhance responses to treatments, and support the immune system.

The other key principle used in this book, in addition to overloading cancer cells with amino acids, is to starve them with foods from which they cannot gain energy. You must use only "dog-friendly" **carbohydrates** with animal proteins in order to maintain body weight while starving the cancer. All simple carbohydrates (sugars) must be completely eliminated from an NR diet. In addition, all carbohydrates are reduced and the amounts of foods with protein and **fats** are increased to prevent cachexia and **metastasis** (spread) of cancer. A diet specific to the dog's cancer can help trigger normal immune system functions, strengthening the immune system. Understanding nutrition is an integral approach for cancer treatment in order to provide the maximum benefits for dogs.

How the rest of this book is organized

Chapter 2 – An Overview of Cancer in Dogs

An overview of cancer provides information for dog owners so they will gain knowledge about the disease. It includes the early warning signs, causes, and types of cancer, as well as treatments for cancer. Cancer cachexia is defined, with an explanation of the phases for early diagnosis. Importance of constant monitoring of the phases of cachexia is stressed for changes in treatment and nutrition planning. Cachexia is as dangerous as the disease of cancer.

Chapter 3 – A Nutrition Regimen (NR)

Our NR is presented with a systematic plan for integrating diet, feeding, and weight management for dog owners and veterinarians. It includes advice for dog owners about how best to collaborate with veterinarians to develop a prescribed course of treatment and diet for dogs with cancer. A Standard of Nutritional Intervention is initiated with the NR establishing a level of quality for nutrition for dogs with cancer

Chapter 4 – Metabolism of Carbohydrates, Proteins and Fats

Chapter 4 focuses on the metabolism of carbohydrates, proteins and fats, each thoroughly discussed. You must understand the metabolic changes caused by cancer so that you can formulate the cancer diet for your dog. Foods for each nutrient are listed in the **nutrition regimen diet**.

Chapter 5 – Fish Oil and Omega-3 Fatty Acids

Chapter 5 is a comprehensive discussion of omega-3 fatty acids— eicosapentaenoic acid (EPA) and docosahexaenoic acid (DHA)— establishing the importance of omega-3 fish oil. It is considered the single most potent supplement you can add to your dog's diet. Guidelines for purchasing human grade, omega-3 fish oil supplements are detailed. Table 5.1 recommends safe maximum daily doses of combined EPA and DHA omega-3 fatty acids.

Chapter 6 – Medicinal mushrooms

Chapter 6 highlights the use of **medicinal mushrooms** as a supplement with strong anti-cancer effects. Medicinal mushrooms recommended for treatment are described in this chapter with explanations of which ones are safe for dogs. Additionally, guidelines for purchasing medicinal mushroom supplements are detailed.

Chapter 7 – Arginine

Chapter 7 reviews arginine, an essential amino acid that must be present in your dog's food. It greatly enhances the immune system and helps immune cells attack cancer. Arginine slows the growth of most cancer and metastasis to other parts of the body. Many dogs may have surgery, and arginine decreases inflammation and improves wound healing. Enhancing nutrition with arginine is a must for the dog's diet. Table 7.1 list foods high in arginine for planning of a nutrition regimen menu.

Chapter 8 – Selenium and Food Content

Chapter 8 provides a discussion of selenium, a trace mineral that is essential to the dog's diet. It fights to defend the dog's body against cancer. There is a significant loss of selenium during periods of stress caused by cancer and cancer treatments. Foods rich in selenium are listed in Table 8.1.

Chapter 9 – Glutamine and Food Sources

Chapter 9 details the role of glutamine, the main amino acid in dogs. It must be included in their diet. Glutamine accounts for over half of amino acids in blood, brain, organs, and muscle tissue and thus, plays a critical role in the functions of the immune system. Food sources and supplements are provided in the chapter.

Chapter 10 – Vitamins and Minerals

Chapter 10 includes a description of the vitamins and minerals that are required by all dogs for optimal functioning and to sustain life. They must be added to their food when preparing a homemade diet. There are seven vitamins needed by dogs for a healthy lifestyle: vitamin A, B complex vitamins, vitamin C, vitamin D, vitamin E, vitamin K, and choline. Each vitamin and mineral is discussed, with a description of the benefits for dogs. Foods are recommended as excellent sources for vitamins and minerals.

Chapter 11 – Probiotics

Probiotics are live microorganisms or good **bacteria** in the dog's body. They aid in maintaining balance between good and bad bacteria. They have been referred to as the "building blocks" of the immune system. Cancer and chemotherapy cause tremendous changes in the dog's diet and may cause vomiting or diarrhea. Probiotics help keep a balance of the bacteria population in the colon and are vital for optimal functioning for your dog's health. Benefits of probiotics and standards for probiotic supplements are discussed in Chapter 11. **The nutrition regimen steps** provide direction for you and your veterinarian for selection of the best probiotic supplement.

Chapter 12 – Nutrition Regimen Menu

This important and practical chapter provides suggested ideas for planning and preparing appetizing and nutritional meals. It gives ideas for creating daily or weekly menus for your dog's yummy dishes. A menu of dishes with savory names—instilling enthusiasm for meal planning—is designed for individualized breakfast, lunch, and dinner. Menu descriptions list the special ingredients for cancer diets, as tools needed for management of nutrition treatment plans.

It is not intended to give you recipes for your dog's meals, rather to encourage and stimulate ideas. Special food and cooking preparations are suggested to provide appetizing and healthy dishes. It gives control to dog owners for total nutrition and diet planning. Mealtime should become a fun time for you and your dog with preparation of the tasty dishes.

Chapter 13 – Home Care

Chapter 13 outlines accommodations in the home to provide the most comfortable environment for your companion during stressful times. Because dogs in treatment may have decreased appetites, it is very important to understand the **palatability** of food, which is also discussed in this chapter.

Afterword – Toward A Standard of Nutritional Intervention

A brief look at the strides made in the field of canine nutrition over the past few decades and what we believe we have achieved in this book to further that progress going forward.

Backmatter

Cited works, a glossary, an appendix which includes a listing of good dog food recipe books, information about the authors, and an index are included in the back of the book. Words included in the glossary are shown in bold where they are first mentioned in the text.

Chapter 2
Overview of Cancer in Dogs

Cancer cachexia

Cancer cachexia is an extremely dangerous condition caused by the disease of cancer. It results in rapid weight loss and loss of both fat and muscle even when caloric intake is adequate. Cachexia can be present with all types of cancer. It continues during remission of cancer and must be continually guarded against. Cancer cachexia is a complex syndrome affecting many dogs with cancer. New interest in this area has allowed for research that is becoming increasingly important in veterinary medicine. Increasing awareness of cancer cachexia has led to the development of new treatment options including nutritional in nature.

Diagnosis

Early diagnosis is critical; however, it can be difficult to make. Loss of body weight is not a good way to measure muscle loss. This lack of diagnostic criteria decreases the ability to identify cancer cachexia. The dog may reach an advanced stage of cachexia before it is noticed. The result can be an under diagnosis of the condition since the identification of cachexia in its early stages is extremely difficult when relying on body weight.

Changes in metabolism

Cancer alters the metabolism of carbohydrates, proteins, and **lipids**, resulting in cachexia. After remission is obtained from chemotherapy or other treatments, problems with **metabolism**, the body's use of nutrients, are still present. Adaptations required to switch to fat utilization are not present, resulting in **amino acids** (the building blocks of proteins) being used as a primary source of energy. This process leads to the continued loss of lean body mass or muscle.

The profound alterations of metabolic responses of dogs with cachexia result in progressive weight loss. In addition, the dog suffers from fatigue, **anorexia** (loss of appetite), chronic nausea, decreased activity level, and depression. These changes in metabolism can be diagnosed in the early stages of cancer. Dietary therapy may be effective for the treatment of cancer cachexia.

Phases of cachexia

There are three phases associated with cancer cachexia. The first phase is the preclinical "silent" phase. It is where the dog is not exhibiting any clinical signs of the disease. There are biochemical changes indicating high lactate, high insulin, and alterations of the amino acid and lipid profiles. The alterations of carbohydrate metabolism are profound, with the production of tremendous amounts of lactate through energy-inefficient anaerobic metabolism. Lactate is the end product of anaerobic metabolism. The second phase is when the dog begins to exhibit weight loss, anorexia, lethargy, and early evidence of muscle loss. The dog most likely will be exhibiting side effects from surgery, treatment with chemotherapy, or radiation therapy. The third and final phase of cachexia is associated with marked debilitation, muscular weakness, and biochemical evidence of negative nitrogen balance. Dogs lose carbohydrate and protein stores within the body. Loss of fat deposits is noted in the final stage. The dog is wasting away due to the physical effects of cancer and cancer-induced alterations in metabolism.

Diet can help!

You may be able to prevent cachexia by adopting some elements of the diet recommended later in this book to treat cancer. For example, feed dog foods that contain salmon and tuna for their omega-3 content. I also add blueberries, spinach, and pumpkin, all anti-oxidants.

If your dog is stricken with cancer, begin feeding him to prevent cachexia instead of waiting for a diagnosis. Once there are clear signs, it may be too late. Feed your dog a high-quality diet and cook for them using the plans offered in this book. Involve him in food preparation and give him a lot of attention at mealtime. His appetite may not be great, and it is up to you to find foods that he will eat. You will have to change his diet often! Make feeding time exciting for both you and the dog. It is necessary for survival time. You must establish a nutrition plan with your veterinarian early in a cancer diagnosis.

Early warning signs

Early detection

Your dog may not have been diagnosed with cancer; however, you have probably read about early detection being very important in treatment. Appointments with your veterinarian are usually annual. As a pet owner, there are early warning signs of cancer that you can recognize at home between these appointments. Pay attention to your dog. If he does not get up and come to greet you like usual, then something is probably wrong. **Lethargy** is not a sign of tiredness. If his usual level of excitement about interactions with you is missing or they seem lethargic (lacking in energy), then further examination is needed. If your dog becomes less active, it is for a reason.

Lumps and bumps

Dog owners should perform a monthly lump check. Lumps and bumps under a dog's skin are not to be ignored and require a trip to the veterinarian. Abnormal swelling under the skin that continues to grow must not just be watched. Sores that do not heal are also a concern.

Swollen glands or cough

Swollen glands in the throat area may be a warning sign of a cancer called lymphoma. They could also be an indicator of infection, but they should not be ignored. Coughing is not an immediate sign of cancer, but after several days it is a concern worth discussing with your veterinarian.

Oral cancer

Any unexplained sores, bleeding, or odors in the mouth can be a sign of oral cancer. Daily tooth-brushing routines can provide the opportunity to examine the mouth and nose more closely. Gums are usually a bright pink. If your dog's gums become pale or suddenly turn white, then take your dog to a veterinarian! Bleeding from the mouth or nose is never normal.

Weight loss

Unexplained weight loss due to cachexia may be the number one sign of cancer in dogs. Loss of appetite is always a distress signal; however, dogs may lose weight even when maintaining the same appetite. It usually means the presence of a tumor in the intestines. Your dog will stop eating when they feel pressure or stomach pain. Your dog should never just start shedding pounds.

Bathroom habits

Changes in bathroom habits should be noted. You know what is normal for your dog. There should be concern over a loose stool or diarrhea. Occasional diarrhea is most likely not a sign of cancer. Bloody or tar-colored stools, hard stools or straining are symptoms of problems you should speak with your veterinarian about.

Breathing or respiration

Sudden changes in your dog's breathing or respiration are alarming warning signs. They mean your dog is in distress or pain. Coughing could accompany breathing problems. You cannot ignore this sign. Heavy panting when your dog is not exercising or unusually warm usually means your dog is experiencing some distress and pain.

Seizures

If your dog has a **seizure** (a convulsion due to electrical misfiring in the brain), it can be a sign of a brain tumor. An uncontrolled, strong, jerking or chewing of paws and foaming of the mouth is a seizure. Take your dog to the veterinarian immediately. This is an emergency! Seizures are usually seen in older or senior dogs but take them seriously regardless of age.

Swollen areas

When you are spending time with your dog, be aware of any unexplained swollen areas. Examine the area to see if there is sensitivity to touch or pressure, a growth, or if the area is painful. Watch your dog and see if the swelling disappears or returns. If it is determined to not be a symptom or changes relating to cancer, then you can just monitor it. If there is any question in your mind, then it needs to be checked.

Limping

Your dog may hesitate to exercise with you or display a limp when you go for a walk. You may know the signs of unusual stiffness or arthritis commonly seen in older dogs, but lameness is different. It probably will not go away. Examine the paws for foreign bodies or look for swelling in the foot or leg. When the behavior becomes persistent, it must not be ignored. Your dog's eyes will show the discomfort and pain.

Causes of cancer

Genetic predisposition

One out of ten dogs will die of cancer each year. Genetics alone is not always the primary cause, but it is often a contributing factor. Heritable risk is not assigned to a single gene. It seems to follow complex patterns that indicate the interaction of many genes.

Lifetime risk and incidence of cancer are different among distinct breeds of dogs. Certain breeds of dogs tend to be more susceptible. Among the breeds with the highest rates of cancer are Golden Retrievers, German Shepherds, Labrador Retrievers, Rottweilers, Boxers, and Beagles.

There is heritable predisposition to different kinds of cancer. However, cancer may occur due to impacts to the genes during your dog's lifetime that were not present at birth. These may result from internal or external factors such as pesticides, tobacco smoke, **obesity**, or even sunlight.

The National Canine Cancer Foundation suggests that risk for some types of cancer is related to genetic mutations that are more common within certain breeds. This is due to the fact that the American Kennel Club requires that registered dogs must be a relative of other dogs of that breed. This creates an isolated, closed population within each breed. The gene pool is small, allowing these mutations to flourish within them. There is also the "popular sire" result where certain dogs are bred over and over again. Genetic outcomes, good and bad, are spread to many generations of a breed of dogs.

There may be a positive effect for this process of breeding. It may provide a unique opportunity to identify heritable factors that could be manipulated to reduce this risk, and which would be difficult or impossible to identify in other species.

Immune system depression

The immune system is the dog's protector from diseases. Cancer patients have depressed immune functions. The essential role of the immune system is to maintain the dog's overall health and resistance to disease. Immune competence is provided and maintained by two cellular systems involving **lymphocytes**. Lymphocytes are natural killer cells produced by the body's primary (bone marrow and thymus) and secondary (lymph nodes and spleen) lymphatic organs. B-cells derive from bone marrow and T-cells are produced in the thymus. Dogs mainly have B cell lymphoma.

The connection between chronic stimulation and chronic overstimulation of the immune system is particularly important. We know the two systems work together to produce conditions necessary for cancer development. The National Canine Cancer Foundation lists a weakened immune system as a contributing cause of lymphoma. Metabolic changes that occur with cancer are permanent even when cancer is in remission. Cancer places great stress on your dog's immune system. Chronic exposure to drugs and chemicals, steroids, chemotherapy, and the existing problem of your dog's cancer highly stress the immune system. Poor diet and nutrition also reduce the effectiveness of the immune system.

Pesticides

Dogs are exposed to many different chemicals. Flea and tick repellents fed to dogs or applied to their bodies are the most common chemicals that may be potential causes. Carpets are often cleaned with chemicals for flea control (Harper, 2019); (Dobbins, 2020); (Kaneene, 1999); (Natural Resources Defense Council, 2009).

Dogs living in homes that were professionally treated with garden pesticides were about 70% more likely to get lymphoma. Round Up—directly linked to lymphoma—is a commonly used pesticide in yards where dogs often play, lie, and roll. Dogs then tend to clean and lick themselves, allowing them to swallow the poisons. Any herbicide, insecticide, or pesticide may be harmful to your pet (Dobbins, 2020); (Kaneene,1999); (Yin, 2017).

Spaying/neutering

The most common cancer preventive step is to spay or neuter your dog. Female dogs rarely develop **mammary cancer** if spayed. In male dogs neutering eliminates the risk of testicular cancer.

Obesity

Obesity is the most preventable and most common disease in dogs. Over 40% of dogs are above their ideal body weight, and obesity is especially prevalent in dogs aged 5-11. If a dog weighs 20% more than their ideal body weight, they are considered obese. Dogs who are overweight have a shorter life expectancy by as much as two years, and they experience increased medical problems.

Obesity is associated with an increased risk for many types of cancer. Fat tissue is biologically active secreting inflammatory hormones that contribute to many diseases. Obesity may be thought of as a chronic, low-level inflammatory condition. Inflammation may be thought of as the new pet obesity.

Obesity is within human control. When your dog's energy intake exceeds their energy demands, obesity results. Simply stated, when you overfeed your dog and they don't get enough exercise, overweight conditions are the result. Weight gain may also occur in dogs for whom treats are readily available, or when palatable foods are given in place of or in addition to regular meals.

Obesity in dogs is preventable. If your dog starts to gain weight, cut back on the food. Do not free feed and allow your dog to graze. Give your dog discrete meals, not all-day snacks. Measure the food with a measuring cup. Eyeballing food portions is not accurate. Weigh your dog often, and if your dog is putting on pounds, cut back on portions. Following the feeding instructions on the bag of food is a starting point, but keep in mind that energy requirements vary with breed, neuter status, and medical conditions. If you are training with treats, count these as part of your dog's daily intake of food. Your dog needs daily exercise. If you are not exercising, your dog probably is not getting enough exercise.

Second-hand smoke

Living with humans who smoke can cause cancer in dogs. They breathe second-hand smoke just like humans. Moving the smoking outside does not prevent them from breathing the carcinogenic agent, which can be brought back in on a person's clothes and skin and transferred to upholstery or directly onto the dog.

Ultraviolet radiation

Continued exposure to ultraviolent through excess sun exposure is a problem for many dogs, especially those with white or light-colored coats. Their skin is very sensitive to sunburn, and as in humans, it may cause cancer. Animals living outside carry more risk for skin cancer.

Types of cancer

Cancer is unrestrained cell growth and cell division that is not regulated as with normal cell division. The result is a tumor. There are six major types of cancer: lymphoma, mast cell tumors, melanoma, **osteosarcoma**, **hemangiosarcoma**, and mammary cancer.

Lymphoma

One of the most common types of cancer in dogs is **lymphoma**, cancer of the lymphatic system. The dog's lymphatic system is primarily responsible for transportation of lymph throughout the body. It is made up of small glands called lymph nodes. It is a vital system for participating in the immune functions of the body. The lymphatic system carries proteins and other substances away from tissues of the body. Lymph nodes are filled with white blood cells containing lymph fluid. They provide a site for white blood cells to mount an immune response, preventing foreign substances from getting into the bloodstream.

Dogs with lymphoma usually do not show symptoms until the disease has been present for some length of time. Usually, the owner will notice swelling in the lymph nodes in the neck or throat area. When your dog develops lymphoma, the cancerous cells start dividing rapidly, causing the lymph glands to swell. During a routine brushing or bathing of your dog, you may discover the lymph nodes under the neck are swollen or enlarged. Other lymph nodes are located behind the shoulders and behind the knees, and can occur in the spleen, liver, and other organs. Your dog may not seem sick at all. Routine check-ups by your veterinarian are usually where lymphoma is discovered.

Lymphoma appears in the white blood cells, lymph nodes, bone marrow, spleen, liver, and the gastrointestinal tract. A dog's survival rate is dependent on whether the cancer originated in the B-cells or T-cells. The more common and more treatable type of lymphoma is

B-cell. Most dogs with T-cell lymphoma succumb to cancer. Dogs diagnosed with B-cell respond much more favorably to conventional treatments and usually go into **remission** (a temporary cure), which correlates with increased survival time. However, lymphoma is the most responsive to chemotherapy.

Lymphoma is classified into stages to provide more information about how far the disease has spread in the dog's body (Freeman, 2019); (Modiano, 2009). It is a way of determining the best treatment. The stages also help provide a sense of effectiveness of treatments. Effectiveness is related to likelihood of remission and life expectancy. During staging, any other medical problems that could affect the prognosis or alter the treatment plan can be ruled out. The World Health Organization (WHO) classifies lymphoma into the following stages based on its degree of metastasis and progression:

Stage I: Involves a single lymph node in a single organ

Stage II: Regional involvement of multiple lymph nodes

Stage III: Generalized lymph node involvement

Stage IV: Involvement of the liver or spleen

Stage V: Disease present in bone marrow, blood, central nervous system or other organs

Lymphoma is the most treatable of all types of dog cancer. However, it is not a curable disease. After initial detection, the cancer, if untreated, will progress quickly and kill a dog within one to three months. With appropriate treatment, many dogs experience remission for an extended period of time, usually 12 to 18 months. During remission, no signs of the disease can be detected by tests, and dogs can live a healthy and seemingly cancer-free life.

Mast cell tumors

Mast cell tumors are a type of skin cancer common in dogs. The tumors are found in the skin, intestines, and respiratory tract tissues. These tumors contain histamines and **enzymes**, substances that normally protect the body. However, when a mast cell tumor develops, that protection turns against the immune system. Mast cell tumors are graded according to their location, presence of inflammation, and how they have grown or transformed.

Melanoma

Melanoma is the most common malignant tumor. These tumors are usually found in the dog's mouth or lip areas. They can also be found in the pads of the foot, nail beds, and eyes. At first sight, melanoma may appear as a swollen paw, or a sore near or in the mouth or eye that starts draining. The tumors are very aggressive and grow deep into body tissue. A melanoma can invade body organs.

Osteosarcoma

This is a type of bone cancer. It is more common in larger breeds. The cancer is usually malignant and grows rapidly. Signs of osteosarcoma include swelling of limbs or lameness.

Hemangiosarcoma

This type of cancer is highly malignant. It arises from the cells that line blood vessels of various tissues of the body, allowing blood to seep into the abdominal cavity or chest cavity. It is most often found in the heart or spleen. It spreads very rapidly anywhere in the dog's body.

Mammary cancer

This cancer is found most often in female dogs that were not spayed or not spayed by the age of two. Approximately half of these cancers are malignant and have spread to other areas of the body. It is usually found around the nipples of the dog.

Treatments

Surgery

The first line of treatment for localized cancer that can be removed is surgery. If total removal of the cancer is uncertain, treatment becomes a difficult decision. All options and outcomes should be completely understood before a treatment plan is chosen.

Chemotherapy

Your dog is in oncology treatment for some type of cancer or is recovering from surgical procedures. You must decide what is right for your pet and for you. You will be informed of the diagnosis, protocols, treatment procedures, and prognosis for dogs with cancer. You will learn about the risks of treatments, survival time, and quality of life for your dog. When your veterinarian recommends chemotherapy you, like many people, may believe the process will be scary and will involve horrible side effects when, in fact, it can be very effective and save your dog's life.

Chemotherapy is any cancer treatment that works by killing off cancerous cells. It can be delivered intravenously or orally. The risk of side effects from chemotherapy is relatively small. Dogs tolerate these treatments much better than people, in part because veterinary oncology places a strong emphasis on quality of life during treatment. Most dogs are not in pain during treatment, and they do not lose their hair or get sick.

The most advanced and recommended chemotherapy treatment is the **"CHOP" combination therapy**. It is considered the "gold standard" of current lymphoma care for dogs. The protocol for the chemotherapy is from the University of Wisconsin-Madison School of Veterinary Medicine. The protocol combines three chemotherapy drugs, Vincristine, Doxorubicin, and Cytoxan. In addition, prednisone is also used during early care. It is a 25-week treatment plan. At the end of six months if your dog achieves remission, treatment is stopped with hopes of a long remission. The disease should become unnoticeable pretty soon after treatment is started.

A high percent of dogs achieve remission very early in treatment. Once your dog falls out of remission, a new cycle of treatment of may be started (Chun, 2009); (Couto, 2013); (Freeman & Ulbrich, 2019).

Cost of chemotherapy treatment should be considered. Examinations, blood tests, and cost of the drugs vary depending on the size of your dog. Travel is usually involved because of the types of chemotherapy and the need for intravenous treatment. The drugs are almost always given only in a veterinary oncology office so travel may be extensive. Generally, most oncology veterinarians recommend the Madison Wisconsin Protocol for Lymphoma. Forethought should be given to money, time, and location for treatments. Factors including the type and stage of cancer also must be taken into consideration.

Your veterinarian will likely recommend that vaccinations not be administered during the period when your dog is receiving chemotherapy, because they can cause deleterious results. Your dog has probably been vaccinated for years and has long-term immunity.

Most veterinarians do not want to complicate your pet's already stressed immune system by giving them viral vaccine antigens to deal with in addition to cancer. If you are concerned about compliance with state regulations, ask your veterinarian to write a letter providing documentation of long-term vaccinations, especially if you have plans for travel during your dog's chemotherapy.

Radiation therapy

Radiation therapy is considered a localized treatment to achieve tumor control. It prevents the replication or dividing of cancer cells by bombarding them with radiation. It is useful to target tumors that are locally aggressive and cannot be completely surgically removed. Doses of radiation therapy are controlled to prevent or minimize harm to normal tissue and to minimize side effects. The goal of treatment is to reduce the adverse effect the tumor is having on a dog's body and maximize survival time and quality of life.

Immunotherapy

Immunotherapy is a treatment using the body's natural defenses to fight cancer. It uses materials made by the body to restore immune system function. It is now being utilized more frequently to protect the dog's immune system instead of weakening it with chemotherapy.

Research into effective cancer immunotherapy is making remarkable strides. There is increased awareness of the dog cancer immunotherapy model. Cancer is made more manageable with these new technologies and advancements. Enhancing the dog's natural defenses offers potential advantages over traditional cancer therapies. Treatments act to assist the immune system identify which cells are cancerous. Infusions with immune cells, such as lymphocytes, represent one of several modalities of immunology. Working to stop or slow the growth of cancer cells and stop the spread of cancer to other parts of the body is the major goal of immunotherapy. This antibody therapy will not replace traditional chemotherapy, but instead it will complement treatment protocols and potentially improve outcomes. However, immunotherapy is also costly and outcome measures require close follow-up, leading many owners to discontinue treatment early.

Palliative care

Palliative care is an approach when the disease has progressed to a life-limiting illness. Your dog's activities of daily living should be identified and monitored as part of ongoing assessment of their quality of life. Pain management is the most important consideration in palliative care. Medications, nutritional supplements, and non-pharmacologic therapies may be suggested to alleviate discomfort, but the goal is not halting or reversing the progression of disease. Medical acupuncture, massage, chiropractic adjustment and physical therapy are common therapies during palliative care.

You may want to make your home more comfortable for your dog. Assisting with balance and maximizing mobility by adding nonskid floor surfaces is an option. Raising food and water dishes or placing dishes near your dog will minimize the risk for falling and reduce pain when eating or drinking. Make comfortable spaces close to the family so your dog can spend time with those they love. The goal is to improve the quality of life for you and your dog.

Complementary and alternative medicine

Complementary and alternative medicine is becoming increasingly popular. The terms complementary, alternative, integrative, and holistic are used interchangeably to mean non-conventional therapies. To form a treatment whole, your veterinarian may recommend surgery and drug therapy from conventional medicine along with alternative techniques. Alternative treatments are intended to work with the natural healing mechanisms of the body to fight cancer. The focus is on a total or whole body approach. Exercise, nutrition, mind-body massage, petting, mindfulness, acupuncture, herbal medicine, supplements, changes to the home environment, homeopathy, and veterinary chiropractic are a wide variety of therapeutic modalities.

Your dog is highly attuned to your stresses so practicing mindfulness as a dog owner may have an impact on your dog's quality of life. Your dog is very perceptive about your feelings or anxiety. Do your best to stay positive and have a happy outlook. The dog-human bond is not fully understood, but research suggests that dogs would rather get our praise than treats or food. Your dog loves to feel your touch and massage. Try to focus on the moment with your dog while remaining prepared for future outcomes.

Chapter 3
A Nutrition Regimen

Knowledge of the relationship between nutrition and health continues to advance for dogs with cancer. It is important to base feeding choices on good information. Based on this information, pet owners and veterinarians can develop specialized diets for individual dogs. Feeding your dog an appropriate amount of a well-balanced diet is vital to her overall health and well being. All dog owners must answer the question, "Does the food I'm providing meet the nutritional needs of dogs with cancer?"

Dogs need several kinds of nutrients to survive. Under normal circumstances, dogs can meet their nutritional needs from plant and animal foods. The six basic nutrients are water, proteins, fats, carbohydrates, minerals, and vitamins. These essential nutrients are required by all dogs to build and maintain tissue and carry out biological functions. The source of the proteins and fats is less important than the quality and digestibility of these essential components of the dog's diet. For dogs with cancer, this picture changes dramatically.

Our NR presents a systematic plan, process, steps, and menu to establish an optimal standard of nutritional intervention for widespread use by dog owners and veterinarians. It is a means to support a prescribed course of treatment and a diet for the promotion of health. Menus can be prepared from essential nutrients and food ingredients.

Science-based research
Our NR is a science-based program for dogs with cancer, providing nutrition that meets the standards of veterinarians and works within

the abilities of dog owners. State-of-the-art research by Gregory Ogilvie (1995-2006) established nutrition as a key component for treatment and control of cancer. His landmark research provides the foundation for a nutrition regimen. The diet must be developed for your dog, not for the cancer.

Ogilvie and other research colleagues were granted the U.S. Patent (US5776913A), a therapeutic diet for dogs with cancer. This innovation was based on the discovery that metabolic disturbances in animals with cancer are mitigated by feeding a nutritionally balanced food composition. Ogilvie (1998) focused on a "cancer diet." The diet was composed of small amounts of complex carbohydrates, minimal quantities of rapidly absorbed simple sugars, high-quality, but modest amounts of digestible proteins, and certain types of fats. His research established the first dog's diet in combination with chemotherapy to eliminate clinical evidence of the cancer and slow the progression of the disease.

Research was so compelling that Dr. Ogilvie worked with Hill's Science & Technology Center to create dog food specifically formulated for the needs of the cancer-stricken dogs, Hill's Prescription Diet. It was marketed in 1998 after a decade of study. This nutritional concept was backed up by hundreds of studies in lab animals, people, and dogs. Metabolic changes that occur in a dog with cancer were shown to be permanent, even if the cancer went into remission. Feeding an adapted diet was shown to be necessary for the remainder of the dog's life.

While optimal nutrition was found to be a key component for treatment of cancer and for helping control the disease, early detection of cancer was also crucial. Ogilvie's research showed that abnormalities in metabolism are altered long before cancer is detected through visible symptoms; these changes exist regardless of the type of cancer. Dog owners and veterinarians must be aware that nutritional intervention should begin before cancer cachexia becomes evident. The earlier the intervention, the better the outcome. If you wait until weight and strength begin to plummet, you are in trouble.

The American Cancer Society sponsored a landmark study on quality of life, disease-free interval time, and survival time of dogs with cancer. The study was on the effect of fish oil, **arginine** (an amino acid), and doxorubicin chemotherapy on remission, survival time, and selected aspects of metabolism and the immune system for dogs with lymphoma. These dogs have abnormal elevations of lactic acid and insulin, leading to cancer cachexia, decreased survival time, and decreased time to recurrence. It was noted that this appears to be the first time that a diet supplemented with n-3 fatty acids and arginine has been shown to improve disease-free interval and survival in an outbred species with cancer.

Ogilvie's "cancer diet" (Ogilvie, 2000) recommended the following nutrient percentages:

- 37% animal protein
- 32% fat – mostly animal sources
- 21.6% carbohydrates
- 3.5 omega-3 fatty acids
- 2.5% DHA fatty acids
- 3.4% arginine (amino acid)

Ogilvie's research is supported by colleagues recommending that the dog's cancer diet should be less than 25% carbohydrate, 35-48% protein, 27-35% fat, 5% omega-3, and more than 2% arginine. These percentages in the diet need to be adjusted based on individual needs and health of the dog. The NR outlined in this book also includes selenium, glutamine, vitamins, minerals, and probiotics. There will be an ongoing adjustment to these figures as a dog responds or fails to respond to the diet. Each dog is unique. What is nutritionally sound for one dog may be inadequate for or even harmful for another.

Dog owners and veterinarians are faced with challenges when supporting dogs during and after cancer treatment. It must be determined what foods and supplements work best for your dog. Guidelines for foods are recommended with 30 to 40 % of the calories coming from good quality protein sources, 50 to 60% of the calories coming from fat, and the rest of the diet from carbohydrates. Veterinarians can estimate how many calories your dog needs based on stage of cachexia, phase of cancer, health status, and body condition score. Weight must be carefully monitored, due to cachexia, as loss of appetite and fatigue can affect caloric needs.

The American College of Veterinary Nutrition (Marion, 2014); (Saker, 2014); (Saker & Selting, 2010) has provided detailed information on practical approaches by foremost nutrition specialists.

One of the most significant issues that can arise during cancer treatment in dogs is malnutrition. Dogs experience side effects when undergoing common oncologic therapies. Malnutrition significantly decreases response to treatment protocols and remission time. Malnutrition can result in poor wound healing, altered immune system response, fluid and electrolyte imbalances, as well as the body weight changes associated with cachexia.

There is no cure

There is no dietary cure for cancer; however, a "cancer diet" in combination with chemotherapy and other treatments can slow the progression of cancer. In some cases, this diet can improve the dog's quality of life, improving health by preventing cachexia from nine months to a few years (Ogilvie, 2000-2006). Nutritional intervention must be aggressive! Carefully selected nutrients and planned food selections can be used as powerful tools to reduce toxicity associated with chemotherapy and strengthen the immune system.

Nutrition regimen

Our NR plan is a system for integrating diet, feeding, and weight management for meeting nutritional and treatment needs of dogs with cancer. A diet can be tailored to fit the individual needs of the dog, and healthy ingredients for cancer diets are provided as tools to develop food menus. The NR plan empowers dog owners to make the best decisions with their veterinarian for nutrition intervention with appropriate diet planning. Dog owners and veterinarians can develop nutrition programs that promote quality of life and improve survival time.

Our NR process entails actions for dog owners to collaborate with veterinarians to develop a prescribed course of treatment and diet for promotion of health. Some veterinarians are considered nutrition specialists. However, most veterinarians are not educated in the nutritional qualities of ingredients that encourage healthy cell growth and discourage the growth of cancer cells. Enhanced nutrition is of unquestionable benefit to any dog with cancer. Options for diets and supplements are fairly consistent for the types of cancer. Again, diet or supplements cannot "cure" cancer, but the best hope is to support the immune system to keep the dog in best health and to help keep a dog in remission who is receiving treatment. Simply staving off weight loss can be a critical factor in survival for the dog.

An integrated approach is suggested for cancer survival, treatment, recovery, and living with advanced cancer. Diagnoses should include type, stage of cancer, health and nutritional status, and phase of cancer cachexia. Clearly defined goals for treatment outcomes empower dog owners to make the best decisions for their dogs. The concerns for every dog with cancer include preserving lean muscle, minimizing metabolic and gastrointestinal (GI) intolerance to food, and optimizing the dog's quality of life.

It is helpful for owners to begin consultation with their veterinarian with an understanding of the most promising advances in the science of treating cancer through nutrition. This allows for you and your veterinarian to know the complete clinical picture with access to laboratory reports during nutritional intervention. Dogs receiving therapeutic nutrition need to be monitored by a veterinarian to ascertain whether other concurrent diseases are playing a nutritional role.

Our NR steps are action measures for dog owners and veterinarians to develop a prescribed course of medical and nutritional treatment to restore and preserve health of dogs with cancer. NR steps provide a structured process to facilitate positive change for dog owners and veterinarians for diet management with menus or daily feeding. These steps are a means to optimize communication and promote nutritional values. Dog owners and veterinarians can follow these steps to monitor appetite, weight changes, and the dog's overall health status during cancer treatment. Goals may be designed for integrating diet, feeding, and weight management. The steps are:

1. Understand the diagnosis of type and stage of cancer.

2. Determine health status of your dog.

3. Decide on cancer treatments.

4. Determine phase of cancer cachexia.

5. Recognize and accept the critical importance of an enhanced nutrition plan.

6. Facilitate and discuss a nutrition regimen diet.

7. Plan systematic strategies for nutritional enhancements.

8. Discuss high or "mega" doses of specific supplements.

9. Develop your specific nutrition regimen menu for your dog's daily feedings.

10. Continue reassessment of your dog's health, weight, and nutritional status.

11. Understand the need for and importance of exercise (e.g., daily walks) with your dog.

12. Continue modification of ingredients and meals as needed in light of health changes.

Our nutrition regimen diet overview

Cancer cells must be starved of any energy sources while essential nutrients are provided to dogs with cancer. Dogs with cancer must be fed a very different diet so they have the essential nutritional requirements. The cancer diet menu should be prepared with foods high in omega-3 fatty acids, protein, and fats. It should be comprised of very low amounts of carbohydrates. Foods containing high arginine, the mineral **selenium**, and **glutamine** (an amino acid) are important. Necessary vitamins and minerals must be included in home-prepared diets. The NR diet includes high amounts of **omega-3 fatty acids** as a food and food supplements. Omega-3 fatty acids are considered the cornerstone and powerhouse of the diet of dogs with cancer. Omega-3 is an essential fatty acid that is almost universally beneficial, providing nutrients to every cell in the body. Dogs cannot synthesize essential omega-fatty acids, so they must have them supplied through the foods or supplements they consume. It is probably the most important and highly used supplement in cancer treatment. Chapter 5 includes detailed research about the benefits of omega-3s, as well as sources of food high in omega-3 fish oil. It also offers advice for the purchase of pure supplements.

Protein

Our NR diet is comprised of 37% animal protein. It should include high quality and easily digestible proteins. Proteins have specific nutritional functions in the dog's body: building of muscle tissue, regulation of **antibodies** (proteins that attack invaders in the body) within the immune system and transfer of nerve impulses. Functional proteins must be **bioavailable** (able to be absorbed into the body), and free of contaminants such as chemicals, hormones, and antibiotics. The less bioavailable the protein source, the more your dog will eat to assimilate amino acids. Dogs must have essential amino acids when they are under higher levels of stress such as cancer and the treatments that accompany it. The amount of protein your dog requires depends on the quality of the protein, the dog's health issues, and age. The menu should include cooked chicken, steak, pork, roasted turkey, and some seafood. Since dogs cannot manufacture essential amino acids, they should never be restricted in the diet. Chapter 4 includes a discussion of the metabolism of proteins, detailed list of foods high in protein, and calories of various foods.

Fat

Our NR diet is composed of 32% fat, mostly from animal sources. Fats supply dogs with the most concentrated and digestible form of energy. Approximately 90-95% of the fat a dog eats is metabolized for energy. Dogs can consume higher amounts of fat than people since they have a greater capacity to burn fat for energy. Fats are an anti-inflammatory source of fuel, and cancer cells do not thrive on energy from sources of fats. Dietary fats are highly bioavailable, digestible and play a necessary role in the absorption of vitamins and minerals. Dogs are carnivores and benefit from animal-based fat and protein. Cooked steak, ground beef, lamb, turkey, and liver are excellent sources of fat. Complete lists of good sources of fat are discussed in the following chapter. The quality of ingredients improves food digestibility and nutrient bioavailability. Fats also improve the taste of foods and make meals more appealing.

Carbohydrates

Our NR diet is based on approximately 20% **dog-friendly carbohydrates**. Some complex carbohydrates can be part of the diet, but simple carbohydrates such as sugars must be completely eliminated from all foods, including treats. Extreme changes occur in the metabolism of carbohydrates. Substantial amounts of energy are gained by cancer, and your dog suffers tremendous energy loss. Dog-friendly carbohydrates include spinach, broccoli, carrots, Brussels sprouts, and cauliflower. Pumpkin, berries, and oatmeal are good to include for the regimen diet. Chapter 4 includes information about the metabolism of carbohydrates and complete lists of safe foods.

Essential amino acids

Our NR diet includes 3-3.5% arginine, an essential amino acid that should be present in the dog's food. Appropriate quantities of arginine decrease inflammation and improve immune system responses. Enhancing diet and nutrition with arginine is of unquestionable benefit to dogs with cancer. Arginine consumed in combination with omega-3 fish oil has a synergistic effect improving symptoms, quality of life, and survival times. Foods containing high amounts of arginine include leaf or chopped spinach, turkey, eggs, pork roast, cooked or canned tuna, and oven-roasted chicken breast. Chapter 6 includes a discussion of the benefits of and a list of foods high in arginine.

For most types of cancer, reducing carbohydrates and increasing proteins, fats, and omega-3 fish oil can slow cancer growth and prevent cancer cachexia. The concerns for every dog with cancer include maintaining body weight, preserving lean muscle, and minimizing metabolic imbalance and gastrointestinal intolerance to food, optimizing the dog's quality of life.

Dog owners must be motivated to provide their dogs' nutritional support when facing cancer. Of all the factors involved in cancer treatment, proper diet and nutrition is the one that dog owners can best control.

The nutrition regimen menu
The NR menu provides ideas for planning and preparing appetizing and nutritional meals. The type of menu is **du jour**, meaning the menu may change daily with special chef preparations. Chapter 12, which contains a list of creative dishes with savory names, is designed for individualized breakfast, lunch, and dinner meals. Healthy ingredients for dogs with cancer are summarized for each menu selection. Mealtime must become a fun time for you and your dog with preparation of yummy dishes.

The NR menu supports a cooked diet with no raw meats. The American Veterinarian Medical Association officially recommends against feeding raw meat-based diets to dogs. Feeding raw diets can carry several potential risks to humans and dogs. Salmonella, E. coli or other disease-causing bacteria can be present in raw meat. After digesting the food, your dog could become a carrier of the diseases. There is a chance of passing bacteria to other dogs or people the dog comes into contact with. An unbalanced raw diet may damage the health of the dog. When a dog is undergoing chemotherapy treatment for cancer, he does not need his health jeopardized by illness that may be caused by eating raw diets.

Chapter 4
Metabolism of Carbohydrates, Proteins and Fats

Understanding the metabolic changes caused by cancer can help you formulate a diet that provides maximum benefits to your dog. Your dog utilizes carbohydrates, proteins, and fats in very different ways. For many types of cancers, reducing carbohydrates and increasing proteins and fats can slow cancer growth and prevent cancer cachexia. Provide the right nourishment for your dog, not the cancer. Foods and nutrients can be your most valuable allies, allowing you to slow the growth of cancer and strengthen your dog. Simply increasing the amount of a dog's existing food is not always the right answer to provide the most benefit for your dog. You must provide food made with appropriate ingredients of simple carbohydrates, animal proteins, and animal fats. Always provide your dog with fresh, clean, filtered or bottled water.

The consequences of metabolic changes are permanent. Once your dog has cancer, their metabolism remains altered, even when your dog is in remission. By anticipating the potential negative nutritional impacts of cancer treatment, you can adjust your dog's nutrient profile and potentially avoid some of the side effects. Take charge of your dog's nutritional needs. It is something that you can do to help your dog through treatment for cancer.

Carbohydrates
The most dramatic changes occur in the metabolism of carbohydrates. Cancer cells metabolize glucose from carbohydrates, forming **lactate** (the ionic form of lactic acid), as a waste product. Dogs must

expend energy to convert lactate into useable forms. Lactate becomes a poison stealing energy from your dog who has cancer.

The diet must be comprised of a low amount of simple carbohydrates. Ogilvie evaluated dogs with lymphoma to determine if a diet high in carbohydrates is detrimental compared to a diet high in fat. In this study, the dogs were randomized and fed either a high-fat diet or a high-carbohydrate diet before and after remission was attained with doxorubicin chemotherapy. After the dogs were put into remission with chemotherapy, the mean lactate and insulin levels from the dogs fed the high-carbohydrate diet were significantly higher than the level from the dogs fed the high-fat diet. Dogs with significant alternations in metabolism of carbohydrates can develop cancer cachexia. These alterations in metabolism have the potential to decrease quality of life, reduce response to therapy, and shorten survival time.

Simple carbohydrates are sugars that can't be broken down into any simpler form of sugar that needs to be minimized. Glucose and fructose are examples of **monosaccharides**. Honey is one of the most glucose-rich foods. Lactose is a form of sugar found in milk products. During processing of foods, sugar is added to enhance flavor, texture, and shelf life. Added sugar goes by many names and most consist of glucose or fructose. The most common type is sugar or sucrose. Other names, sometimes tricky to spot, include corn syrup, agave nectar, beet sugar, molasses, brown sugar, buttered syrup, cane sugar crystals, cane sugar, caramel, coconut sugar, powered sugar, fruit juice, honey, and maple sugar. Simple carbohydrates lack vitamins, minerals, and fibers. Foods high in simple sugars include dates, watermelon, pineapple, apples, ice cream, milk products, bread, cakes, pies, candy, pastas, and some cereals. Read labels carefully on all packaged foods and eliminate all sugars often found in treats. Cancer thrives on simple sugars. The listing below is of some simple carbohydrates that must be eliminated from the dog's diet.

Foods with Simple Carbohydrates That Dogs with Cancer Can Not Eat:

- Table sugar
- Grain products
- Dates
- Honey
- Caramel
- Brown sugar
- Sugar coated cereals
- Milk products

- Agave nectar
- Molasses
- Watermelon
- Apples
- Fruit juice
- Bread
- Maple sugar
- Corn syrup
- Powdered sugar
- Pineapple
- Pastas
- Cakes and pies

Cancer cells utilize simple carbohydrates found in grains and starchy vegetables as well. These ingredients should be reduced or eliminated in your dog's diet. Avoid grains, like corn, wheat, and rice, found in many commercial dog foods. Instead, select vegetables with fewer sweet carbohydrates and add vegetables with suspected cancer-fighting ingredients such as broccoli, cabbage, spinach, Brussels sprouts, cauliflower, and tomatoes. Chlorophylls (the substance that makes plants green), found most plentifully in dark greens, help protect against carcinogens. The list below provides a list of some foods containing the carbohydrates that are good for dogs with cancer.

Dog-Friendly Carbohydrates:

- Cruciferous vegetables (several included in this list)
- Eggs
- Carrots
- Spinach
- Blueberries
- Zucchini
- Peas
- Cauliflower
- Pumpkin
- Parsley
- Cranberries
- Broccoli
- Cabbage
- Brown rice
- Kale
- Bok Choy
- Bananas
- Oatmeal
- Brussels sprouts
- Watercress
- Cherries

Proteins

Proteins are a very important part of dog food, but not understood by most owners. Protein supports muscle mass, and its depletion saps critical strength. Protein is a substance that contains amino acids, the building blocks of muscle mass. The two classifications for amino acids are essential and nonessential. Dogs cannot manufacture essential proteins in sufficient quantities. Nonessential proteins are proteins that the dog's body can manufacture in sufficient quantities. It bears repeating that both essential and nonessential proteins have specific nutritional functions in the dog's body: building of muscle tissue, regulation of antibodies within the immune system, and transfer of nerve impulses.

Dogs with cancer metabolize protein differently, causing amino acid imbalances. The resulting progressive loss of strength and energy can be a detriment to survival. Protein cannot be restricted for any amount of time and should be provided in the highest available quality. Research (Govier, 2019) suggests that early correction of cancer-caused amino acid imbalances (particularly insufficient arginine and glutamine) leaves dogs better able to survive.

Amino acids that should be present in the diet are arginine—an immune system booster—and glutamine, which support and maintain the health of the GI tract. Arginine slows the growth of tumors and cancer by enhancing immune function. It becomes an essential protein when the dog is under higher levels of stress, or experiencing illness, malnutrition, or injury. Glutamine is an essential amino acid abundant in the skeleton, muscles, and blood. It seems to protect normal cells from the effects of chemotherapy while enhancing the die-off of cancer cells. It reduces gastrointestinal toxicity of some chemotherapy drugs and may minimize inflammation of the intestinal tract. Foods high in cancer-fighting proteins include chicken, beef, tuna, salmon, turkey, pork loin, veal, cottage cheese, and pumpkin. Canned tuna and salmon in oil also have high amounts of protein.

It should be remembered that the idea of overloading cancer cells with amino acids they don't want and starving them of ones they do has proven to be a viable approach to cancer. High-quality and easily digestible proteins are the best source of these amino acids and must be included in the dog's diet. High-quality is defined as the protein having sources that are functional including dairy, eggs, fish, muscle meats, and organ meats. Proteins must be bioavailable and free of hormones, chemicals and antibiotics. Proteins should be minimally processed, not promoting food intolerance. The amount of protein your dog requires depends on the quality of the protein and the dog's health issues and age (Dodds, 2015).

Nutritional interventions should be carefully planned to include specific nutrients for dogs with cancer. It is highly stressed that the cancer diet should include animal protein (39%), carbohydrates (21%), omega-3 fatty acids (3.5%), and DHA fatty acids (2.5%). Prepared foods must also include essential vitamins and minerals. An important consideration when it comes to nutrition is making sure that the calorie and essential nutrient needs are met. Dogs, on average, need about 30 calories per pound of body weight per day to maintain current weight. The goal is to maintain weight. Table 4.1 provides the protein and calorie content that is most beneficial for dogs. It is based on a 3-ounce cooked serving of food.

Table 4.1
Protein Content and Calories of Protein-Rich Foods

Food (cooked)	Protein (g)	Calories
Meat, Poultry, Eggs		
Chicken	28	141
Steak	26	158
Turkey (roasted)	25	135
Lamb	23	170
Pork	22	122
Ham	14	139
Egg	7	75
Seafood		
Salmon	22	99
Tuna	22	99
Shrimp	20	101

Protein = 4 calories per gram

Fats

Fats are a highly bioavailable form of energy for dogs. As noted above, highly digestible food provides a higher proportion of absorbed nutrients than a less digestible food. Digestibility provides some measure of a food's nutritional values and quality. As the quality of ingredients in the food increases so will the food's digestibility and nutrient bioavailability.

Cancer cells do not thrive on energy from fat sources. Increasing dietary fat does not appear to benefit cancer. The dog's ability to use fats as an energy source is not altered, and again, cancer does not thrive on energy from fats. However, 90 to 95% of the fat that a dog eats is metabolized for energy, making fats the most optimal form of energy for dogs because they efficiently process them. In addition, fats are an anti-inflammatory source of fuel for dogs. Therefore, including fats in your dog's diet is a must. Dogs are carnivores and benefit from animal-based fat and protein. Steak, ground beef, lamb, chicken, pork, and liver are excellent sources of fats. Omega-3 fatty acids (found in fish oil) should be increased dramatically. Omega-3 supplements reduce or eliminate some of cancer's metabolic alterations.

Table 4.2 on the next page provides the fat content and calories included in the most beneficial foods for dogs. It is based on a 3-ounce portion of a boneless, cooked food.

Table 4.2
Fat Content and Calories of Fat-Rich Foods

Food (cooked)	Total Fat (g)	Calories
Meats, Poultry, Fish		
Chicken breast (with skin, baked)	7.5	189
Chicken breast (without skin), baked	3.0	130
Chicken (dark meat)	3.0	170
Salmon	7.0	150
Beef (ground)	11.0	210
Beef tenderloin (trimmed of visible fat)	9.0	180
Beef sirloin (trimmed of visible fat)	6.0	170
Lamb chops (trimmed of visible fat)	8.0	180
Pork loin rib chop (roasted)	8.0	190
Dairy		
Egg (large)	5.0	75
Cottage cheese (14 oz., 1% fat)	14.0	81
Cheese string (1 piece, nonfat)	6.0	50
Mozzarella (1 oz.)	7.0	72
Cheddar (shredded, ¼ cup)	6.0	90

Fat = 9 calorie per gram

(Learning Library, 2013)

Nutritional considerations

Provide an appropriate diet for dogs based on low carbohydrates (starches), high quality and easily digestible proteins and high saturated fats. Your dog is highly dependent on what you feed them. Do not feed your dog junk foods. Avoid all fried or greasy foods including potato chips, french fries, and corn chips. Avoid foods with chemical preservatives. This means no cookies, candy or cupcakes no matter how energetically your dog begs for the treat.

The following considerations are recommended for homemade meals:

1. Foods should be fresh, easily digested, highly palatable for your dog and organic.

2. Meats must be high-quality, fresh, and smell and taste good.

3. Vegetables should be fresh, cruciferous, dark green, leafy vegetables such as spinach, kale, cabbage, broccoli, and bok choy.

4. Fish oil (omega-3) supplements should be included with every meal.

5. Vitamin C should be provided daily. It can be easily given in pill form and is an antioxidant.

6. Digestive enzymes supplements are recommended because they provide support to the dog's digestive system during treatment for cancer.

7. Garlic in very small amounts includes ingredients whose organic components are effective inhibitors of the cancer process.

8. Olive oil should be used to cook special meals.

9. Limited carbohydrates should be fed.

The National Institutes of Health and the American Institute for Cancer Research recommend mixing vegetables into foods as the best way for dogs to accept them.

Carbohydrates are limited to those not containing any form of simple sugar. Make an optimal support plan with your veterinarian to formulate a diet that meets the dog's specific needs, especially during chemotherapy treatment. The plan should include goals determined for each dog and their individual needs. Metabolism of the dog will continue to be affected by cancer, even during remission, so the importance of meeting the dog's nutritional needs cannot be stressed enough for quality of life and length of survival.

Making every meal very special is important and gives you personal time with your dog. For pets to accept some of the tastes of the vegetables, some owners choose to use a food processor. Meals may need to be blended so the savvy and somewhat picky eater cannot leave undesired vegetables uneaten. The best way that you can be assured that you are providing your dog with the best diet possible is to cook it fresh each day. Involving your dog in the process of food preparation allows the smells of the foods to increase your dog's appetite. Do not put your dog's food dish on the floor and walk away. Take time with your dog during mealtime. When your companion is not feeling at their best, it may be necessary to entice your dog to eat by hand feeding. You may find that chemotherapy changes your dog's appetite for some of their favorite foods. You may be challenged to provide the best freshly prepared foods daily, as well as changing the menu often to keep a healthy appetite.

Chapter 5
Fish Oil and Omega-3 Fatty Acids

Fats mainly derived from animals provide a concentrated source of energy in dogs. They supply essential fatty acids that cannot be synthesized in the dog's body. All nutritional fats are composed of fatty acids. These fatty acids are referred to as essential fatty acids. Dogs require the Omega-3 fatty acids eicosapentaenoic acid (EPA) and docosahexaenoic acid (DHA), which are the most powerful. Omega-3 fatty acids may be considered the cornerstone of the dog's nutritional plan. Dogs must have these fatty acids supplied through the foods they eat. Dietary fats carry important vitamins and they enhance the taste and texture of the dog's food.

Why supplements?
Dogs cannot readily produce omega-3 fatty acids, and most dog foods do not have adequate amounts of fish oil so supplements may be required. EPA and DHA fatty acids can only be found in the flesh of cold-water fish. Omega-3 fatty acids (fish oil) are probably the most common supplement added to the diet of dogs with cancer. Omega-3 fatty acids are a canine super food, regulating cellular metabolic functions. Omega-3 is one of the single, most potent supplements you can add to your dog's diet. Fish oil supplements are a highly used conventional medication. In general, more severe diseases require doses higher than those commonly recommended.

Groups of fatty acids
Fish oil is made up of many healthy long-chain polyunsaturated fatty acids. The two primary groups of fatty acids are omega-3 and omega-6

fatty acids. The diet must be enriched with omega-3 fatty acids for dogs with cancer. Omega-3 fatty acids, EPA and DHA, appear to prevent the growth of some cancers. Omega-6 fatty acid is important for all animals to stay in good health. However, omega-6 fatty acids suppress cells that are key in the body's natural cancer-fighting ability. If your dog is diagnosed with cancer, eliminate dog foods containing omega-6 including the ingredients beef fat (lard, tallow), corn (grain, oil, meal), vegetable oil, sunflower oil, and soybean (Dressler, 2018).

Benefits of omega-3 fish oil

Omega-3 fatty acids reduce inflammation, fight cancer, and benefit the immune system. It slows or even inhibits the development and metastasis of certain cancers. Remember that metastasis is the process of cancer spreading to other parts of the body. The ingredients, EPA and DHA in fish oils, seem to prevent the growth and development of cancer and cancer-related complications via suppression of the inflammation process (Pask & Scott, 2018); (Freitas & Campose, 2019).

Omega-3 fatty acids from fish oil strengthen the immune system, the dog's protector from disease. Cancer places great stress on the dog's immune system, but proper immune function leads to an overall better response to chemotherapy treatments. It is necessary to provide appropriate nutrition and supplements to support immune system effectiveness. Poor nutrition reduces its productivity and efficiency (Ogilvie, Fettman, and Malinckrodt, 2000).

Omega-3 fatty acids have been shown to inhibit growth and metastasis of cancer (Ogilvie, Fettman, and Malinckrodt, 2000); (Pask & Scott, 2018). Supplementation of the diet with EPA and DHA omega-3 fatty acids was used to evaluate whether omega-3 could improve metabolic parameters, decrease chemical indications of inflammation, enhance quality of life, and extend disease-free interval and survival time for dogs treated for lymphoma. Arginine and fish oil were shown to reverse changes caused by complications of cancer. Dietary supplementation with arginine and fish oil resulted in significant increase in serum arginine and n-3 fatty acid concentrations. Results indicated that dogs had an increase in disease-free intervals and survival time. Omega-3 fatty acids also reduce the effects of cancer-related complications such as cancer cachexia.

Omega-3 fatty acids may exert beneficial effects on dog behavior, although the precise mechanism is not understood (Lenox, 2021);

(Lewellen, 2016). Diet and nutrition may have a positive impact on unwanted behavior in dogs. New treatments focused on these supplements have been proposed for anxiety and depression. Increased dosage of fish oil has a calming effect from both a behavioral and physiological standpoint. There is evidence to support using fish oil as a potential reliever of depression, anxiety, and hyperactivity in numerous species, including dogs (McGowan (2016); (Wall, 2018). Fish oil has been found to influence the same pathways as medications commonly prescribed for treatment for anxiety disorders in dogs. Dogs receiving chemotherapy experience stress, anxiety, and depression. Increased doses of omega-3 fish oil as part of an appropriate nutrition plan should help with anxiety and depression caused by cancer and its treatment.

Purchasing omega-3 fish oil

It is very important to purchase pure, human-grade fish oil supplements. You do not want to give dogs with cancer fish products or fish oil supplements that may be contaminated with industrial pollutants or other toxins. Do not substitute flaxseed oil, which can be a source of omega-3 fatty acids, as it does not contain EPA and DHA.

When purchasing fish oil, make sure fish oil ingredients are unaltered and free of environmental or other undesired toxic elements. The best fish oils are always processed and manufactured by reputable companies. They use natural sources and are tested thoroughly for harmful or undesirable contaminants. There should be no artificial fillers, binders, or synthetic components. Additives like rosemary extract as a preservative, and gelatin and glycerin-based capsules, can interfere with effectiveness. Some lower-priced or generic fish oils use poor-quality oils and contain mercurial particulates or pesticide residues.

Omega-3 fish oil packaging should state on the label that ingredients include high amounts of EPA and DHA with natural fish oil. Omega-3 fish oil should specify the exact levels of EPA and DHA. The standard for EPA/DHA levels in fish oil should total a minimum of 500 mg per serving. Always check the label to ensure that EPA/DHA levels are clearly listed.

Dosage

The National Research Council (2006) publication on Nutrient Requirements of Dogs recommends a safe upper limit of combined amounts of EPA and DHA (not total omega-3). It is recommended to start with approximately one quarter of the maximum dose of omega-3 for 100 to 150 mg per 10 pounds of body weight daily (Dodds, 2015). Fish oil supplements can be purchased at most health store. Your veterinarian can help you determine the amount of fish oil to feed your dog or recommend a suitable fish oil product for them.

Table 5.1 lists safe maximum daily doses of combined EPA and DHA omega-3 fatty acids. Dog's weight is in pounds and kilograms, and combined EPA and DHA are in milligrams.

Table 5.1
Safe Maximum Daily Doses of Combined EPA and DHA
(Not total omega-3 dosage)

Dog's weight (lbs)	Dog's Weight (kgs)	EPA and DHA (mgs)
5	2.3	684
10	4.5	1,150
15	6.8	1,559
20	9.1	1,934
25	11.4	2,286
30	13.6	2,621
35	15.9	2,943
40	18.2	3,253
45	20.5	3,553
50	22.7	3,845
55	25.0	4,130
60	27.3	4,409
65	29.5	4,682
70	31.8	4,949
75	34.1	5,212
80	36.4	5,470
85	38.8	5,725
90	40.9	5,976
95	43.2	6,223
100	45.5	6,467

Read labels carefully for the amounts of safe maximum daily dose of combined EPA and DHA. The appropriate type of omega-3 fatty acids can provide powerful benefits for the health of dogs with cancer. Sources for omega-3 fatty acids must be high in EPA and DHA. You should be able to tell from your dog's stool if you are giving too much fish oil. The stool will appear softer than the usual.

Food selection

Sources of omega-3 include cold-water fish like salmon, herring and mackerel. Darker-fleshed fish such as herring, salmon, mackerel, and bluefish generally have a higher total fat content than lighter-colored flesh such as cod, flounder, and pollock. The darker, oilier fish tend to have the highest level of omega-3 fish oil. The following table includes foods with high amounts of omega-3 fatty acids (Cleveland Clinic, 2019; Seafood Health Facts, 2019). These foods serve as key ingredients for the NR diet.

Table 5.2
Foods High in Omega-3 Fish Oil

Fish and seafood source 3 oz. (85 grams)	Total omega-3 fat (grams)
Mackerel	2.5-2.6
Herring	1.3-2.0
Salmon (Wild)	1.8
Trout (Lake)	2.0
Tuna (Bluefin)	1.2
Bluefish	1.2
Sardines	2.0
White Fish (Fresh Water)	1.2
Oysters (Wild & Farmed)	0.5-1.0
Swordfish (Wild)	0.5-1.0

Preparing the diet with natural sources is the safest way to feed your dog. However, it can be costly and difficult to find appropriate sources. It should be noted that your dog may not like or tolerate fish well. Omega-3 fish oil may need to be used as a supplement.

Canned seafood products are a viable option to add fish oil to the dog's diet. The amount of total omega-3 fatty acids can vary in species of fish and shellfish. Table 5.3 includes frequently consumed canned seafood products with amounts of omega-3 fish oil in cooked portions of a 3-ounce can (USDA National Nutrient Database for Standard Reference, 2019). Canned food products may be easily prepared adding omega-3 fish oil to the dog's diet. This table will help with planning for your purchases for meals.

Table 5.3
Canned Seafood Products

Canned seafood product (3 oz.)	Omega-3 cooked portion (grams)
Salmon (Pink, Sockeye & Chum)	1.0 -1.5
Mackerel (Jack)	1.0 -1.5
Tuna (Wild Bluefin)	1.0 -1.5
Tuna (White Albacore)	0.5-1.0
Sardines	0.5-1.0

Side effects of fish oil
Fish oil supplements may have side effects in some dogs. Adverse effects are likely to be dose dependent. The anti-inflammatory effect of EPA and DHA decreases platelet activity and aggregation, reducing the dog's ability to form clots. This effect could cause dogs to suffer higher blood loss during surgery or if injured. EPA and DHA anti-inflammatory properties may interfere with the wound healing process and the body's production of new skin.

The inflammatory responses of the immune system are important to effectively control infections, cancer, and other abnormalities. Excessive amounts of EPA and DHA may interfere with these processes. For treatment of cancer, the dosage may be increased where the risk of side effects is less important than the benefits of treatment. Your veterinarian will be able to help you with dosage and any possible side effects.

Gastrointestinal effects can occur, but the effects are dose dependent. Recommendations for managing abnormal stools or diarrhea include slowly transitioning the dog to a high dosage of an omega-3 fatty acid supplement. Dogs may need other dietary modifications as well.

Weight gain is not a commonly noted effect of omega-3 fatty acid supplementation. In obesity-prone dogs, the calories of fish oil should be considered in the nutrition plan. However, since cancer cachexia is a major complex syndrome affecting many dogs with cancer, any weight gain from the extra calories of fish oil is most likely a benefit for dogs with cancer.

Chapter 6
Medicinal Mushrooms

Medicinal mushrooms are mushrooms that are used for medicine; they are used worldwide to fight cancer and enhance the immune response. They are considered miracle plants for natural healing of your dog. They contain hundreds of medicinal properties including being antioxidant, anti-tumor, and providing immunity revitalization. They are capable of both preventing and reversing the progression of cancer. Historically, mushrooms were cultivated from forests where they grew naturally. Almost all widely used medicinal mushrooms are artificially cultivated today. Wild mushrooms could be poisonous, so never allow your dog to eat them.

The main ingredients in medicinal mushrooms are natural compounds called polysaccharopeptides (PSPs), and the more important are called **beta-glucans**. They have profound immune invigorating and anti-cancer effects. Compounds extracted from certain types of mushrooms may prevent normal cells from turning into cancer cells. Treatment strategies were studied in complex animal models (Brown & Reetz, 2012). PSPs were examined to determine metastasis of cancer and survival effects of canine hemangiosarcoma. A polysaccharide compound extracted from the *Coriolus versicolor mushroom* (turkey tail mushroom, cloud mushroom, Yunzhi mushroom) from China has been used in herbal medicine for over 2,000 years. It is important to mention the brand name when stating PSP use in research studies because different brands can have varying amounts of polysaccharides. The PSP compound, I'm-Yunity, used in the study is composed of 46% polysaccharopeptides and 31% soluble protein. Quality control of I'm-Yunity involved testing by laboratories at the manufacturing site and by independent commercial centers. This dietary supplement may offer antitumor effects, inhibit growth of tumors, and enhance immune-stimulating properties. Data suggest that when the cancer patient does not have advanced treatments available, PSP as a single agent may offer significant improvements in survival time and quality of life (Brown & Reese, 2012); (Dodds, 2015); (Richter, 2017).

The medicinal mushrooms recommended for treatment of cancer in pets are reishi (*Ganoderma lucidum*), shiitake *(Lentinula edodes)*, maitake *(Grifola frondosa)*, turkey tail *(Coriolus versicolor)*, chaga *(Inonotus Obliquus)*, and *Cordyceps* mushrooms. The benefits of each are discussed here.

Reishi *Ganoderma* mushroom (the mushroom of immortality)

Reishi is used in traditional Chinese medicine for cancer treatment to improve strength, vitality, and stamina, and to prolong life. It is one of the most respected immune longevity supplements in the world. It provides support by stimulating the immune system and activating lymphocyte activity. The reishi mushroom is an antioxidant giving anti-tumor support. It has the ability to stop certain cancer growth. Reishi alleviates the side effects of chemotherapy and decreases inflammation. Quality of life is greatly improved (Scott, 2018); (Sean, 2018).

Shiitake *(Lentinula edodes)*

Shiitake contains a glucan called active hexose correlated compound (AHCC) and is widely used for its immune-enhancing functions. The shiitake mushroom contains 30 different enzymes and 10 amino acids. It also contains the minerals calcium, zinc, magnesium, iron, and selenium. They reduce the side effects of chemotherapy and radiation. Shiitake mushrooms reduce inflammation (Jennings, 2019).

Maitake *(Grifola frondosa)* cloud mushroom

Maitake cloud mushrooms are used in traditional Chinese and Japanese medicine to enhance the immune system. Maitake mushrooms contain beta-glucans, vitamins B, C, and D, antioxidants, amino acids, copper, potassium, fiber, and minerals. The maitake mushroom may be more effective than any other to inhibit tumor growth. It is one of the major mushrooms that protects cells with its antioxidant properties. The maitake mushroom fights to decreases the inflammatory response and to potentially decrease metastatic properties inhibiting the spread of cancer. It is also used to treat the side effects of chemotherapy. Dogs experience weakened immune systems from cancer, infection, and inflammation. Maitake mushroom-based supplements provide a booster for the immune system. It may work best when combined with other compounds of the reishi, shiitake and turkey tail mushrooms (Basko, 2010); (Chilkov, 2017); (Lehman, 2017); (Marsden & Messonnier, 2009); (Scott, 2019).

Turkey tail *(Coriolus versicolor)* mushroom

Turkey tail mushrooms are a highly researched medicinal mushroom. They are packed with antioxidants, compounds that inhibit damage caused by oxidative stress. Turkey tail mushrooms stimulate the release of protective compounds that promote the health of the immune system and reduce chronic inflammation caused by cancer. They contain immune boosting polysaccharopeptides that fight infection and suppress the growth of some cancers. Turkey tail mushrooms are the best overall mushroom for cancer prevention and enhance the efficacy of chemotherapy. They also contain bacteria that improve digestion and GI health (Basko, 2020); (Kubala, 2018); (Sean, 2018).

Chaga *(Inonotus obliquus)* mushroom

Chaga mushrooms, known as birch conk, provide great nourishment for the immune system. They have the unique property of not only boosting the immune system, but slowing down an overactive immune system. Chaga mushrooms help the immune system target cancer cells. They are high in glucans and are loaded with antioxidants. Chaga mushrooms have anti-inflammatory effects and reduce toxicity of chemotherapy treatments. They may prevent cachexia and maintain healthy body weight by aiding digestion (Brunty, 2020); (Sean, 2018).

Cordyceps mushroom

Cordyceps mushrooms are immune boosters like the other mushrooms, but *Cordyceps* also greatly strengthen and benefit the dog's respiratory system. They help dogs overcome the stress associated with cancer and chemotherapy treatment. *Cordyceps* help with muscle atrophy, weakness, fatigue, and confer vitality. They slow the progression of cancer and tumor cell growth. Combinations of organic Reishi and Turkey Tail are suggested to reduce inflammation (Basko, 2018); (Marsden & Messonnier, 2009); (Sean, 2018).

Purchasing medicinal mushroom supplements

It is important to know which mushrooms are considered safe for dogs as a supplement and to understand the benefits of each supplement. Since you are working with your veterinarian, ask what is recommended for your dog's health and if you should consider a medicinal mushroom supplement as part of the treatment plan. The following are suggested guidelines for purchasing mushroom supplements (Grocycle, 2019); (Whitechurch, 2019):

- The supplement must contain 100% mushroom fruiting body. Read the fine print on the nutritional facts label. The product should not contain any mycelium, the mushroom root system, or myceliated grain (a fungal root system that has been allowed to grow on grain but not develop into full mushrooms). Mycelium has lower potency than actual mushrooms. It is an FDA requirement that herbal products and supplements say specifically the part of the plant the product is made from, or list other unimportant ingredients. It may be advertised as "full spectrum" containing all parts of the mushroom including the caps, stems, or mycelium.

- The label should confirm the product's content and quality with actual testing documentation. The documentation must include a strict and rigorous analysis of products including testing for heavy metals, aflatoxins, radiation, pesticide residues, or microbiological contaminants (like yeast, mold, *E. coli*, Salmonella, or *Staphylococcus aureus)*. Polysaccharopeptide may be a grain or starch and does not always mean beta glucans are present.

- The company should state clearly what you can expect from the product. It should include guaranteed potency confirming the percentage of beta glucans and other nutritious compounds like antioxidants, probiotics, amino acids, proteins, flavonoids, and digestive enzymes.

- Concentrated mushroom extract is superior to a powdered product. However, powdered extracts are easier to use and mix.

- The product should be certified organic, guarantee cleanliness, and have a high nutrient content. Know where the product comes from. If you are unsure, call or email the company and ask to see the standards and the testing results for their mushrooms to back up claims.

- Starch is a filler. The amount should be listed in the ingredient.
- Match the health benefit you are looking for in a medicinal mushroom supplement.
- How was the dosage determined? Is it safe to use during pregnancy?

Medicinal mushrooms are considered a dietary supplement. It may be necessary to ask the manufacturer these questions: Has this product undergone clinical trials for safety and efficacy of the product? Are there standards for verification of the product? Has a dosage been determined? Is the supplement safe for all life stages, including pregnancy? Has quality testing been done to guarantee the product?

Chapter 7
Arginine

Arginine is an amino acid that should be present in the diet of dogs with cancer. There are three types of amino acids: semi-essential, essential, and nonessential. Arginine is synthesized as an intermediate in the **urea cycle pathway** and is also obtained from dietary proteins. Thus, arginine is considered a semi-essential amino acid. Arginine becomes an essential amino acid when the dog is under higher levels of stress, illness, malnutrition, or injury. By enhancing healing, inflamattion, and immune responses, it slows the growth of tumors and cancer (Pletcher, 2018).

Research supporting arginine

The American Cancer Society sponsored model research on arginine by Gregory Ogilvie (2000). Participants in the study were pets whose owners brought them in for cancer treatment. The study provided dogs with one of two diets supplemented with arginine and fish oil (experimental diet) or an identical diet supplemented with soybean oil (control oil). Diets were fed before and after remission was attained with doxorubicin therapy. Abnormal elevations of lactic acid and insulin in their blood indicate cachexia, decreased survival time and decreased time to recurrence. By normalizing levels with arginine and fish oil, the researchers were able to reverse these trends and significantly increase survival time. Dogs fed the experimental diet had longer disease-free intervals. Concentrations of arginine were reported to improve wound healing, inflammation, and immune responses. The growth of tumors was decreased. This study supported the use of arginine and fish oil to slow the development of cancer and maintain the quality of life during chemotherapy treatments.

Research of individual amino acids in dietary portions established the importance of amino acid balance and imbalance in nutrition (Harper, 1958). This pioneering study established that a diet must "provide each indispensable amino acid in the quantity in which it is required by the animal (p. 1025)." Early correction of cancer-caused amino acid imbalances (in particular arginine and glutamine) leaves dogs better able to survive. The concept of overloading cancer cells with amino acids they do not want, and starving them of those that they want, sets the foundation for a therapeutic approach for cancer treatment. Arginine slows the growth of most cancer.

Benefits of arginine

Arginine helps immune cells that attack cancer. One function of the immune system is to identify which cells are cancerous. Arginine slows the growth of tumors and cancer by enhancing immune function. Many dogs with cancer will have surgery. Post-operative immune system suppression is a result. A diet high in foods with arginine improves wound healing, inflammation, and immune responses. Arginine works to stop or slow the growth of cancer cells and stop the spreading of cancer to other parts of the body. Supplements of arginine improve immunologic, metabolic, and clinical outcomes. Enhancing nutrition with arginine is of unquestionable benefit to any dog with cancer.

Foods high in arginine

Arginine occurs in foods such as dairy, fish, poultry, beef, pork, and other meats. Increasing foods with arginine may decrease the growth of cancer. It is a required and essential amino acid for appropriate nutrition in dogs. Table 7.1 lists foods that contain high amounts of arginine. A description for foods based on 200 calories per serving size is suggested and arginine content is recorded in milligrams. These foods should be selected for the NR menu.

Table 7.1
Foods High in Arginine

Food items	Serving description (Based 200 calorie serving)	Arginine content (mg)
Spinach	frozen, chopped, or leaf unprepared	3,317
Spinach	frozen, chopped, leaf, cooked, drained	2,877
Turkey	light meat, cooked or roasted	3,009
Turkey	dark meat, cooked or roasted	2,561
Pork	sirloin tip roast, cooked, lean & fat	2,570
Pork	cured ham with natural juices	2,533
Pork	chops, cooked, broiled	2,521
Venison	lean, cooked or broiled	2,504
Duck	cooked without skin	2,492
Fish (Cod)	Pacific or Atlantic, cooked	2,615
Fish (Salmon)	cooked, canned	2,458
Tuna	canned	2,632
Tuna	yellow fin, fresh, cooked	2,581
Chicken	breast, oven roast	2,724
Chicken	breast, sliced	2,690
Egg	white, raw, fresh	2,700
Beef	top round steak, cooked	2,403
Beef	chuck pot roast	2,303
Beef	sirloin, ground round	1,790
Lamb	cubed, stew, kabob	1,793

A dog with cancer is under considerable stress. The nutrition you provide for your dog is extremely important. Research (Ogilvie, 2000) has proven that composite arginine and fish oil make a significant difference in remission and survival time, in part by helping to strengthen the immune system. To summarize, arginine is an essential amino acid and a key part of the cancer diet that improves wound healing, inflammation, and functioning of the immunity system.

Chapter 8
Selenium and Food Content

Selenium is a **trace mineral** that is an essential nutrient in the dog's diet. Trace minerals are elements only needed in very small amounts. Selenium is used in the dog's body to produce glutathione peroxidase, an enzyme that serves as a natural antioxidant. Selenium is therefore a powerful antioxidant that fights oxidative stress and helps defend the dog's body from cancer. When normal cells need energy, they burn body stores using a process called oxidation, and **free radicals** are a byproduct of oxidation. Free radicals are highly reactive chemicals that have the potential to damage all major components of cells, including DNA. This damage may play a role in the development of cancer. Selenium, as an **antioxidant** can help counter this process.

If the dog's body does not get enough selenium, or gets too much, there is increased risk of disease or other medical problems; selenium and other minerals can have significant impacts on effects of cancer, weight management, digestion, pain, and depression. Dogs can get proper amounts of selenium from balanced nutrition or supplements.

Sources of selenium

Selenium occurs naturally in soil. However, selenium levels vary from region to region based on farming practices. Foods are a major natural source of selenium, and its levels generally depend on soil selenium levels, which are sometime deficient. The soil used for growing vegetables may be deficient in minerals such as selenium. There is great variability in the nutrient contents of foods raised by industrial agricultural practices when compared to organically raised foods. Insufficient selenium intake can cause many health problems. This prompts many dog owners to search for the most wholesome produce available to include in diets. Since most of us have no way to know what kind of soil our food was grown in, supplementing dogs with selenium and vitamins may be a good idea.

Benefits of selenium

Studies (Messonnier, 2019); (Sharadamma, 2011) have shown a beneficial effect of selenium in the prevention of and protection against some types of cancer. **Antioxidant** properties of selenium reduce the rate of oxidative cell damage caused by chemicals playing a significant role in anticancer functions. There is a significant loss of selenium during periods of stress caused by cancer treatments. Life expectancy is decreased when dogs have insufficient selenium. Supplementation may reduce adverse effects of chemotherapy and decrease the metastasis of cancer.

In addition to its antioxidant properties, selenium is considered one of the critical nutritional factors for normal functioning of the immune system. Selenium deficiencies are reported to suppress the immune response.

There is no bodily process, on the cellular or systemic level, that can operate efficiently without the right amount of minerals. Selenium may increase the effectiveness of vitamin E, an antioxidant that aids in the prevention of cancer and reduces inflammation. Selenium also provides benefits to your dog's body including improved skin and coat condition (it may reduce shedding), joint health, pancreatic function, and lipid absorption. It is also associated with proper thyroid function, reduction of hip dysplasia, slowed aging process of tissues, and prevention of cardiovascular disease. Clearly, selenium is a vital mineral for your dog's health.

Foods high in selenium

The major food sources include grains, meat, poultry, fish, and eggs. Foods rich in selenium are listed in Table 8.1. These foods are excellent choices for preparations of the NR menu. Selenium is recorded in micrograms, one millionth of a gram.

Table 8.1
Foods rich in selenium

Food	Serving size (in oz or cups)	Micrograms
Tuna (yellowfin)	3	92
Sardines (canned in oil)	3	45
Lean pork chop	3	40
Beef round steak	3	33
Turkey (boneless)	3	31
Beef liver	3	28
Chicken (light meat)	3	22
Cottage cheese (1% milkfat)	1 cup	20
Beef (ground)	3	18
Oatmeal	1 cup	13
Spinach (cooked)	1 cup	11
Brown Rice	1 cup	19
Egg (hardboiled)	large	15

(National Institutes of Health, 2018)

Selenium supplements
Selenium supplements supply your dog with the amount of selenium that they need to remain healthy. A deficiency of selenium in foods produced for dogs has been a long-recognized problem. It is thought to be a safe supplement; however, selenium supplements should be recommended by your veterinarian. It is a toxic mineral and is only required in very low doses. There is a narrow difference between its required dose and the toxic dose.

Chapter 9

Glutamine and Food Sources

Glutamine is the main amino acid in dogs. It is considered a conditionally essential amino acid. Glutamine deficiency may result due to injury, infection, surgery, or illness, including cancer and chemotherapy. It must be included in the diet during conditions of extreme stress.

Benefits of glutamine

Glutamine is the preferred energy source of the cells of the mucous lining of the digestive tract. It fuels many of the body's cells, especially the mucous membrane cells lining the mouth, stomach, and intestines. Supplementing with glutamine ensures that your dog has adequate fuel to rebuild these tissues from damage caused by vomiting or diarrhea from cancer and treatment. Glutamine reduces gastrointestinal toxicity from chemotherapy treatments and minimizes inflammation of the GI tract (Dressler, & Ettinger 2011); (Marsden, Messonnier & Yuill 2019); (Richter (2017).

Glutamine also provides support for the immune system, skeleton, muscle **protein synthesis**, blood, and nerve tissues. It accounts for over half of the amino acids in a dog's blood, brain, muscle tissue and many organs. Glutamine has a critical role in functions of the immune system, namely the network of white blood cells, antibodies, and other substances that fight off infections, and reject foreign bodies. It is the major source of fuel for white blood cells. Because glutamine blood levels can decrease due to major injury or surgeries, the function and health of the immune system can be compromised by glutamine deficiency.

The muscular system needs glutamine for high-quality fuel. It is needed for protein synthesis of muscle cells (the process of building muscle mass). Glutamine feeds muscle cells, allowing them to maintain strength. It is muscle fuel and an ultimate source of energy for muscle cells to keep the dog active and moving. Trauma caused from injury or surgery can deplete reserves, particularly for muscle cells. It is of utmost importance to supplement glutamine since it is the major amino acid in dogs.

Glutamine is higher in concentration in the brain and central nervous system than any other amino acid. It serves as a fuel and support for neurotransmission and neurological organization and participates in a variety of metabolic pathways in the nervous system. Despite its many benefits, glutamine can pose a risk to dogs with epilepsy because of its involvement in several neurological and metabolic pathways.

Not to be used for brain cancer
While tumor cells use glutamine as an energy source, research indicates that supplementing glutamine does not promote tumor growth. Glutamine supplementation feeds normal body tissues before cancer tumors receive a benefit, so the benefits of supplementation with glutamine outweigh any concerns, with one exception: In the case of brain cancer, glutamine should not be given to dogs because it can feed brain cancer cell growth.

Food sources
Both animal and plant foods provide a good source of glutamine. While animal proteins are highly rich in glutamine, there are numerous vegetables as well that are also a good source of this amino acid. Consider these foods for the NR menu.

Meats
Meats contain very high amounts of protein. Foods that are high in protein are also high in glutamine. Beef, chicken, turkey, lamb, pork, and venison are excellent sources of glutamine. Lamb has the highest calorie content. Refer to Chapter 4 for all details on meat.

Seafood
Fish is considered a great source of glutamine. Seafood has a high content of glutamine. Salmon, tuna, and shrimp are the seafood richest in protein.

Eggs
Eggs are considered an excellent source of glutamine. They also provide good sources of selenium and protein.

Vegetables
Green leafy vegetables such as broccoli, cabbage, and spinach are good sources of glutamine.

Supplements
Glutamine is a safe supplement, and it does not need a prescription. It is not a highly regulated supplement, so it is best to consult your veterinarian for recommended brands. Some supplements may not contain labeled amount of ingredients. Your veterinarian can recommend dosages for your dog.

Chapter 10
Other Vitamins and Minerals

Vitamins and minerals are essential nutrients found in "balanced and complete" dog foods. They perform specific and vital functions in a variety of body systems and are required for optimal functioning and to sustain life.

Vitamins dogs require

The seven vitamins needed by dogs for a healthy lifestyle include vitamin A, B complex vitamins, vitamin C, vitamin D, vitamin E, vitamin K, and **choline**. The benefits and signs of deficiency for each are as follows (Banfield, 2012); (Dressler, 2011); (Messonnier, 2020).

Vitamin A

Vitamin A is a fat-soluble vitamin responsible for growth and development, cellular functions, and normal activity of the immune system. Muscular weakness and deterioration is a result of a vitamin A deficiency in the diet. It may first be noted via changes in the skin and coat. Foods that are excellent sources of vitamin A include carrots, spinach, liver, pumpkin, fish or fish oil, and eggs.

B-complex vitamins

These vitamins are water-soluble. They dissolve in water. They are carried to body tissues and systems, but cannot be stored in the body. Instead, they are eliminated in urine. Therefore, it is essential that they be consumed in foods or added as a daily supplement. The B-complex vitamins include the following, which provide support for a variety of body functions:

- **Thiamine – vitamin B-1. Thiamine** promotes good appetite and is important in regulating energy and activating functions of the nervous system. The brain and other high-energy organs require thiamine. It is necessary for maintaining a healthy skin and coat. Signs of deficiency are lack of appetite, vomiting, decreased pupil response to light, loss of body movements, and neuromuscular weakness.

- **Riboflavin – vitamin B-2. Riboflavin** plays a major role in physiology and is necessary for cell metabolism. It helps break down proteins, fats, and carbohydrates to release energy, which is transferred to cells as ATP. Vitamin B-2 is heavily involved with red blood cell production and helps to prevent **anemia**. It boosts the immune system. A deficiency in vitamin B-2 results in body weakness, anorexia, and dermatitis.

- **Niacin – vitamin B-3. Niacin** promotes a normal appetite and helps with the digestive process. It is involved with cell metabolism and energy production. Niacin also supports nerve tissues and nervous system development. Symptoms of a niacin deficiency include inflamed lips and gums, black tongue, loss of appetite, and bloody diarrhea. If not treated, it can be fatal.

- **Vitamin B-5 – pantothenic acid. Pantothenic acid** is known as the anti-stress vitamin. It may be useful in the treatment of anxiety and depression. It is involved in the production of adrenal hormones and antibodies produced by white blood cells. Vitamin B-5 enhances stamina and adds to the dog's longevity.

- **Vitamin B-6 – pyridoxine. Pyridoxine** facilitates glucose generation, red blood cell formation, protein synthesis, and is necessary for a healthy nervous system. Vitamin B-6 is essential in fighting inflammation, infections and is supportive for the immune system.

- **Vitamin B-9 – folic acid. Folic acid** is needed for the formation of healthy red blood cells and is important for reproduction. Protein metabolism is dependent on this vitamin. It is effective in preventing weight loss, anemia, and low energy. It provides support for the immune system.

- **Vitamin B-12 – cobalamin. Cobalamin** leads to red blood cell development and is important in preventing anemia.

The vitamin promotes normal growth and development, and is necessary for normal digestion. It is also necessary for food absorption and storage of nutrients, especially by the pancreas. Digestive issues causing diarrhea, weight loss, and seizures can cause a serious B-12 deficiency. Signs of cobalamin deficiency include lack of energy, weakness, loss of appetite, and confusion.

- **Biotin.** This B-vitamin is necessary for fat, protein, and carbohydrate utilization by the dog's body. It is essential for thyroid and adrenal health, strong nervous systems, muscular formation, development of bone marrow, and healthy skin and coat. A biotin deficiency is rare; however, symptoms include scaly skin with lesions, dull hair/coat and hair loss, lethargy, reduced growth rate, diarrhea, and anorexia.

Foods that are excellent sources of B vitamins include liver, green leafy vegetables, beans, and dairy products.

Vitamin C
Vitamin C is a water-soluble vitamin and is rapidly depleted from the dog's body during periods of high stress from excessive work or training, and illness and disease. Supplementation of vitamin C is extremely beneficial for dogs under these conditions and is used for holistic treatments of cancer. A vitamin C deficiency results in bone and muscle weakness, joint pain, and delayed wound healing. Foods providing vitamin C include dog-friendly fruits, vegetables, and organ meats.

Vitamin D
Vitamin D is a fat-soluble vitamin and is extremely important for the use and absorption of calcium and phosphorus. It is stored in adipose and muscle tissue and greatly contributes to bone and extraskeletal health. It facilitates the efficiency of the immune system. It plays a large role in multiple aspects of treatment efficacy and disease prognosis. Foods providing an excellent source of vitamin D include fish, eggs, dairy products, liver, beef, cheese and cottage cheese.

Vitamin E
Vitamin E is a fat-soluble vitamin and is essential for cell function and fat metabolism. It is needed for muscular health. It is a dog's defense against oxidative damage associated with the development

and progression of cancer. Vitamin E food sources are leafy green vegetables, wheat germ, bran, whole grains, and liver.

Vitamin K
Vitamin K is a fat-soluble vitamin instrumental in the activation of blood clotting. It is also beneficial in potential prevention of osteoporosis. It is most often used as therapy for accidental ingestion of rat poison. Excellent food sources are green leafy vegetables, liver, and fish.

Choline
Choline is an essential water-soluble nutrient and is a necessary component of cell membranes. It is neither a vitamin nor a mineral. It impacts liver function, healthy brain development, muscle movement, the nervous system, and metabolism. It is used in the treatment of epilepsy.

Minerals dogs require
Minerals are also considered to be essential for dogs. Macrominerals are required in larger amounts and trace minerals are needed in smaller amounts. Minerals are kept in close homoeostatic balance, involving significant mineral interactions.

Macrominerals
The macrominerals included in the food your dog eats have specific reference ranges established by regulatory and research authorities. The macrominerals include phosphorus, calcium, chloride, magnesium, potassium, and sodium. All these macrominerals are required for cellular functions.

Calcium and Phosphorus
Calcium is the most abundant mineral found in dogs and phosphorus is the second most common. They provide support for healthy bones and teeth. Calcium and phosphorus must stay in close balance. Calcium plays a significant role in the transfer of information between cells and transmission of nerve impulses. It mediates muscle contractions, constriction and dilation of blood vessels, blood coagulation, and secretion of hormones. It is essential to keep calcium at

a steady level. Calcium and phosphorus are found in broccoli, cauliflower, green beans, fruits, and eggs. Sources for phosphorus include all animal meats, eggs, fish, spinach and broccoli.

Sodium, potassium, and chloride

Sodium, potassium, and chloride are electrolytes found naturally in the body that are present as ions, or electrically charged particles. They keep the body's balance of fluid at the proper level. These balances involve maintaining acid-base balance and osmotic balance, transmitting nerve impulses, and facilitating muscle contractions.

Sodium chloride is table salt that may be added to foods. Foods higher in sodium are chicken, cheese, and eggs. Sources of foods for potassium are spinach, broccoli, peas, zucchini, pumpkin, bananas, and leafy green vegetables.

Magnesium

Magnesium is a component of bone, enzymes, and intracellular fluids. It has direct influence on neuromuscular transmissions. Food sources for magnesium include seafood (salmon, mackerel, tuna), spinach, broccoli, peas, green beans, and Brussels sprouts.

Trace minerals

Trace minerals are essential for the dog's nutrition, but they are only needed in very small amounts. Trace minerals play a role in the cellular process for structural and regulatory cellular functions. There must be a proper balance of trace minerals in the dog's food. The five trace minerals your dog needs in their diet are iron, selenium, zinc, copper, and **manganese**.

Selenium

Selenium, the most important trace mineral in the dog's diet, has already been covered in Chapter 8. You'll recall that it is a powerful antioxidant, playing a significant role during periods of stress caused by cancer and cancer treatments. It is critical to the functioning of the immune system for resistance to disease. Insufficient selenium suppresses the immune system and decreases the life expectancy in dogs. Chapter 8 includes the sources and benefits of selenium.

Iron

Iron is an essential component for a number of physiological processes. It is responsible for synthesis of blood and formation of red blood cells and hemoglobin. Hemoglobin carries oxygen and nutrients throughout the body. Iron also is responsible for myoglobin, the oxygen-carrying pigment of the muscles. The best source of food for iron is red meat, including steak and ground beef. Liver is also an excellent source of iron. Dark green leafy vegetables (such as spinach) also provide iron.

Copper

Copper is needed for physiological cell functions. It is necessary for the development and maturation of red blood cells, collagen, bones, and connective tissue. The food sources for copper are liver and leafy greens.

Zinc

Zinc is an immune system booster and enhances the quality of a dog's skin and coat. It is present in foods such as spinach, turkey, and chicken.

Manganese

Manganese is necessary for bone growth and ensures the quality of cartilage. It is also involved in thyroid hormone production. Chicken, salmon, eggs, pumpkin, and spinach are excellent sources of manganese.

Vitamin and mineral supplements

You should always consult your veterinarian about vitamin and mineral supplements. Some supplements help to manage side effects from cancer treatments. Supplements must have credible evidence for providing a benefit to dogs with cancer. Consider each supplement's potential for interactions with other medications, as well as its appropriateness based on the dog's other health conditions, and the type of cancer and treatments.

Some general guidelines for choosing vitamin supplements include:

- Look for brands with clinical studies and actual listing documentation.
- Read labels carefully to ensure safety and quality.

- Be careful of unconvincing evidence.
- Choose brands with confirmed brand expertise.
- Purchase supplements for dogs, not humans.
- Available in practical dosage amounts.
- Reasonable pricing.
- Effective when given orally.

Never use supplements as a substitute for medications or good quality foods. Always consult your veterinarian for quality products and dosage of any supplements.

Chapter 11
Probiotics

Probiotics are live microorganisms thought of as "good bacteria" in the dog's body. The term probiotics means "for life." Probiotics aid in keeping a balance between good and bad bacteria, supporting the systemic work of the body. They have been called the "building blocks" of the immune system and are recommended as part of the NR diet. When your dog's body loses good bacteria, probiotics help replace them. Most bacteria live in the lining of the dog's colon.

A symbiotic relationship

The bacteria in the colon and the rest of the digestive system have a **symbiotic**, or mutually beneficial, relationship with the dog. They survive on the food your dog eats and in turn improve gut health. Several factors can change the dog's digestive tract, upsetting the balance of good and bad bacteria. They include: antibiotics, change in diet, stress, age, parasites, and vaccinations. When a bacterial imbalance or inflammation occurs, the result may be vomiting, diarrhea, constipation, or systemic disease. Probiotics prevent an overgrowth of bad bacteria, keeping a balance of the bacteria population in the colon, which is vital for optimal functioning of the digestive and immune systems, and your dog's overall health.

Benefits of probiotics

Probiotic oral supplements have many benefits, including:

- Preventing the overgrowth of bad bacteria.
- Anti-cancer properties.

- Support of digestion.

- Improvement of immune system functioning.

- Reduction of allergic reactions.

- Support for brain functions.

- Prevention of urinary tract infections.

- Improvement to overall gastrointestinal health.

Bad bacteria that live in the gut have been linked to lymphoma and cancer of the lining of the stomach, colon, and liver. Therefore, probiotics may have anticancer properties because they prevent the overgrowth of bad bacteria. Dogs profit from taking probiotics which boosts the immune system and aids in digestion (Dodds, 2015); (Scott, 2020).

Standards for probiotic supplements

Probiotics supplements are good for all dogs, but especially dogs undergoing treatments for cancer. Chemotherapy causes tremendous changes in what a dog wants or does not want to eat. It may also cause vomiting and diarrhea. Probiotics provide vital support for the gastrointestinal tract and, in turn, the immune system. Probiotics have metabolic, antioxidant, and anti-inflammatory properties crucial for maintaining holistic wellness. There are many probiotic supplements, and it can be difficult to choose the right one. The NR steps provide direction for veterinarian consultation. Probiotics must meet specific standards including:

- Diversity of strains of bacteria

- Contain live, active bacteria

- Formulated for dogs

- Purity

- High potency

The most common types of probiotics contain good bacteria including *Lactobacillus acidophilus* and *Bifidobacterium* (dairy-based products), *Bacillus coagulans* and *Streptococcus thermophiles*. The supplement should contain many strains of bacteria offering a powerful defense against having a sick gut.

Some foods that provide probiotics include yogurt and other dairy products, and fermented foods. Raw goat milk is a much healthier option than cow milk for dogs. Unsweetened kefir is a fermented food, a combination of yeast and beneficial bacteria, and is an excellent source of probiotics. These products help with nutrient absorption and digestion and prevent inflammation.

Chapter 12
The Nutrition Regimen Menu

Our NR menu provides suggested ideas for planning and preparing nutritious meals for your dog. The type of menu selected is one defined as "Du jour," meaning the menus change daily, depending on what is available or the chef prepares. When you follow the NR menu, you will know that what you are feeding your dog meets the nutritional needs for your dog. You will know that you are starving cancer and feeding your dog!

You must become motivated about food preparation and involve your dog in the process. Your dog will gain interest from your enthusiasm and the smells of the appealing food that you are cooking. This will help increase your dog's appetite. You will need to create daily or weekly meal plans for your dog, allowing you to plan for food preparation. It is not intended to give you recipes for your dog's meals, just encouraging and stimulating ideas.

Our NR menu provides a list of dishes with savory names so that you can have fun with your dog during mealtime. In previous chapters, healthy ingredients for cancer diets were provided as tools for management of diet plans. The menu lists specific ingredients including high protein, high fat, omegs-3 fatty acids, arginine, selenium or glutamine. Foods for each ingredient were listed in 3-oz portions with calorie content. Feeding time must be special for you and your dog. It gives control to you for total nutrition and diet planning.

Make mealtime fun!
Put a new spin on naming dishes you will prepare for your friend and say the names with excitement! Your dog can feel your enthusiasm and will quickly learn the names of their new favorite dishes. You must think about fancy foods to make meals into fun times with your dog!

The NR menu begins with suggestions for how to prepare the selected appetizing dishes. Meals may be cooked daily or, when necessary, prepared in larger batches to be used over several days. All foods can be pan-cooked, oven-baked, barbequed, or grilled as a shish kabob on a hibachi. The fancy preparation of foods adds excitement for you and your dog and is a very real part of the regimen!

Cooking with different types of wood provides novel aromas and flavor to foods. Mesquite wood, cedar chips, and charcoal give different aromas and inviting smells. Meal preparation time offers many enjoyable moments with your dog. They get excited when they are involved, and the smells of cooking can be tantalizing. Remember, you can share what you are cooking and spend mealtime with your dog.

Dogs with cancer need several meals daily; this allows for easier digestion. Foods need to be prepared for breakfast, lunch and dinner. You may stick to one food that consistently appeals to your dog or change often to increase their appetite. Preparation should also include snack or treat time. The menu provides ideas to create inviting and healthy meals. Be imaginative and creative to stimulate your dog's interest and make eating very special to everyone involved! Design your own combinations of foods that your dog will eat and are beneficial to them during cancer treatment.

The nutrition regimen menu

Breakfast and snacks

Oatmeal with blueberries
Oatmeal is high in selenium and is a dog-friendly carbohydrate. Remember, selenium is an essential mineral in the dog's diet, serving as a natural antioxidant reducing the adverse effects of chemotherapy, decreasing the metastasis of cancer, and enhancing the immune system. The texture of oatmeal aids in digestion. It can be served as a bowl of oatmeal with blueberries or a baked oatmeal and blueberry cookie. Blueberries have nutrients with potential anti-cancer effects.

Cranberry Oatmeal Muffin

Cooked oatmeal with cranberries can be fed as a meal in the mornings or as a muffin treat throughout the day. Cranberries are high in vitamin C and fiber and are a disease-fighting antioxidant. They slow the growth of cancer and reduce inflammation.

Pumpkin Spice Oatmeal Cookie

Pumpkin is an antioxidant and considered an anti-cancer food. Put the pumpkin into a blender and mix with the oatmeal. Bake into cookies, muffins, or bread. Pumpkin spice can be added as a flavor to foods.

Ginger Oatmeal Tart

Ginger is a safe and beneficial treat for dogs. It aids with digestion preventing nausea and inflammatory issues.

Banana Oatmeal Biscuit

Bananas are a dog-friendly carbohydrate. They contain vitamins B-6 and vitamin C.

Cheddar Omelet

Eggs are a good source of glutamine, selenium, arginine, and protein. Shredded cheddar or mozzarella cheese provides fat for the diet and gives extra flavor for stimulating the appetite.

Lunch

Mesquite Smoked Burger and Broccoli Patti

Beef burgers supply protein, fat, arginine, glutamine, and selenium. Broccoli is highly recommended for good sources of vitamins K, C, B-complex, and E. It also supplies choline, potassium, calcium, and omega-3 fatty acids. Broccoli has excellent antioxidant properties.

Grilled Turkey and Spinach Burger

Turkey provides nutrition in protein, arginine, selenium, and glutamine. Spinach is an anti-oxidant and an excellent source of arginine, selenium, and glutamine. It also furnishes vitamins A, B-complex, C, and K.

Tuna Delight with Peas and Carrots

Tuna is a great source for omega-3 fish oil, protein, selenium, arginine, and glutamine. Carrots and peas are dog-friendly carbohydrates. Carrots are a good source of vitamin A, potassium, and fiber. Peas provide vitamins A, B-1, B-6, C, and K. They are also an antioxidant.

Sardines with Brown Rice and Green Bean

Sardines are very high in omega-3 fatty acids, boost the immune system and reduce inflammation. They are a very tasty treat, making them a good appetite stimulant. Brown rice is a dog-friendly carbohydrate, easily digested, and helps with GI problems. Green beans provide vitamins A, C, and K, calcium, and potassium.

Spinach Soufflé

A spinach soufflé contains spinach, eggs, cheese, and water. Spinach supplies vitamins A, B-complex, C, and K, and is an antioxidant. Healthy resources for arginine, selenium, and glutamine are provided. Eggs supply an excellent protein boost, fat, and selenium. Cheese is high in fat and protein and also provides vitamins A, B-complex, and omega-3 fatty acids.

Dinner entrees

Mesquite-Smoked Steak with Chopped Spinach

Smoke up the grill with mesquite wood for smells and flavor to cook steak and other meats. Steak is high in protein, fat, arginine, glutamine, and selenium. Chopped spinach is a dog-friendly carbohydrate providing vitamins A, B-complex, C, and K. Spinach is also high in arginine, selenium, and glutamine.

Cedar-Smoked Salmon with Broccoli and Pumpkin Biscuits

Mix cedar chips into the barbeque to add flavor to salmon. Salmon is high in protein, fat, and omega-3 fatty acids. It is also an excellent source of glutamine and arginine. Combining broccoli into the meal provides essential vitamins B-complex, C, E, and K. Broccoli is an antioxidant supplying choline, potassium, calcium, and omega-3 fatty acids. Pumpkin is rich in antioxidants and considered an anti-cancer food.

Roasted Pork with Carrots and Banana Bread

Pork is high in protein, fat, glutamine, arginine, and selenium. Carrots are dog-friendly carbohydrates providing sources of vitamin A, potassium, and fiber for the diet. Bananas are a dog-friendly carbohydrate. They contain vitamins B-6 and C, helping with protein synthesis. It makes a flavorful meal.

Grilled Rainbow Trout Filet with Cauliflower and Cheese Sauce

Rainbow trout is packed with protein and essential omega-3 fatty acids. It is high in vitamins B-6 and B-12, selenium, and potassium. It is a metabolism booster. Roasted cauliflower sprinkled with cheddar cheese makes a savory trimming for a meal and is an excellent antioxidant. Cauliflower adds fiber for digestion.

Baked Chicken and Brussels Sprouts

Chicken is an excellent source for protein and fat. It also provides nourishment in arginine, glutamine, and selenium. Chicken contains niacin (vitamin B-3) essential for metabolism of fats. Brussels sprouts are often a favorite of dogs; they are dog-friendly carbohydrates and contain protein. They are sources of vitamin A, B-6, C, D, and potassium.

Use your imagination!

Dog owners will know what foods their dog likes or dislikes. Any suggested menu items may be combined or changed into special prepared meals. Use your imagination and have fun preparing delightful, savory dishes. If they sound good enough to eat, then most likely your dog will feel your energy and enthusiasm and get excited about mealtime!

Chapter 13
Home Care

Feeding your dog healthy, cancer-fighting foods is clearly important and has been the focus of this book since dogs with cancer have different nutritional requirements, and weight loss and cancer cachexia are serious problems. Dogs in treatment may have decreased appetites caused both by cancer and treatments. It is critical to understand the palatability of the foods you provide and to monitor your dog's weight. In your own home, you have control of this part of your dog's treatment plan. In addition to being nutritious, mealtimes should be a quiet, peaceful space for your dog, and as comfortable as possible.

It is crucial that you make mealtime a routine that is enticing for your dog. Our NR diet is designed to engage the sense of smell and taste in dogs. Remember to say the names of the dishes that you are preparing with excitement so your dog begins to really look forward to eating. Do not just place the bowl on the floor or feeding area and walk away! Sit with your dog during mealtime. If your dog shows any signs of discomfort about having you nearby while they are eating, maintain a respectful distance. Resource guarding, protecting their food and water, may come into play. You may even choose to stroke or massage your dog during their meal, as long as this doesn't prove distracting or upsetting to the dog. Talk to your companion so your involvement becomes a routine that you and your dog look forward too. It is a social time that can be very meaningful for you and your dog.

Palatability of food

Understanding the palatability of food is extremely important. It will help you to prepare foods to stimulate the appetite of your dog and encourage eating. Palatability is the capacity of a food or ingredient to stimulate the appetite of dogs to encourage eating and **satiety**, or fullness. It is a measurement of how desirable dogs find their food. Eating is a multisensory experience. Increasing palatability is simply adding anything that offers a significant flavor, smell, or texture enhancement. The smell of the food and food cooking is what first attracts dogs to foods. Dogs can't voice opinions about particular foods. Their "vote" is by consumption of foods. You want to create food that's a feast for the eyes, nose, and palate of your dog.

For most dogs, palatability is increased by introducing novelty or by adding moisture or heat. You must be aware of your dog's tolerance to different foods.

Choose appropriate foods and increase palatability of foods by:

- Increasing moisture with broths or water
- Increasing the smell of food by warming or choosing more aromatic ingredients
- Trying different foods
- Providing quality, fresh food with no additives
- Changing the flavoring of foods
- Providing accessible areas for eating, including raising the dish to a comfortable level, feeding on a non-slippery surface, and keeping the environment pleasant for your dog
- Avoiding feeding when the dog is sick
- Avoid creating an association between medication and foods

Temperature and texture of food

Temperature and texture of foods is very important. If you are warming dishes, allow time for cooling. It may even be necessary to serve chilled foods or at room temperature. Foods that are served to your dog too warm will tend to upset their stomachs. Be aware of textures of food that may be preferred by your dog. Meals are often prepared by mixing several ingredients. A dog's sense of taste is sensitive and may change as he ages and during cancer treatment. It may be necessary to serve foods separately and in smaller portions.

You will need to feed several small and more frequent meals for easier digestion. You must be aware of all food sensitivities and adapt the diet accordingly.

Water

Clean, fresh, cool water must be provided at all times and changed regularly. Glass or porcelain water and food bowls should be used to reduce metallic taste. It may be necessary to provide several water bowls depending on how the dog feels. Wash and clean the water bowls often. Some dogs like to hear the sound associated with cool, clear running water, so involve the dog when filling bowls.

Food aversions

Food aversions, or distaste for a particular food, may develop in dogs with cancer. When the condition occurs, it is essential that you recognize the problem. There is no way to understand why a food is the favorite one-day, and then your dog appears to have no interest the next. Often dogs associate certain smells and tastes of foods with pain, feeling bad, or becoming sick. If you notice a food aversion, a different food should be offered to your dog.

All dogs differ in the symptoms displayed with food aversions. If nausea and vomiting become a problem, do not encourage the dog to eat until symptoms have passed. If the dog drools at the sight of food, turns their head, spits out food, or hides their food, it may be a sign of a developing food aversion.

Medicines for nausea are prescribed for dogs undergoing different cancer treatments. Do not associate medicine time with feeding time, even if food is given with medications. If your dog becomes ill after eating, it may be necessary to change the place you feed them. The dog may associate the area or the surroundings with feeling sick and stay away from food.

Travel

Visits to the veterinarian and oncologist are frequent during cancer treatment. Travel must be planned carefully so that your dog associates trips in the car with pleasurable activities, like walks in the park or travels to pet stores, in addition to veterinary visits. Otherwise, dogs will predict travel to veterinarians and become nervous. It is never too late to start adding fun car rides into your dog's routine to mitigate this possibility.

Allow time for food digestion before putting the dog in the car for a trip to the vet. Set a routine so the dog will know when it is time to travel allowing yard or walks for potty time. Your dog probably already knows your routine of dressing, putting your cap on, picking up a wallet or handbag, and especially when the keys are in hand. These activities let your dog know it is time to go. Tell your dog when they are going or staying at home for the day. Pets know more about our routines than we do! Rushing and putting a dog quickly into the car may prove to be unpleasant for you and your dog.

Exercise

An important part of home care is making time for exercise. It is extremely beneficial for you and your dog. Include special walks for maintaining strength and flexibility. Well-being is generated for both of you through interaction with your dog during walks. Activity will help release anxiety and simply be fun for both you and your dog. The time during exercise will allow you to forget for just a little while about the seriousness of cancer. Remember to give your dog a little massage after exercise. They will love it!

Take everything into consideration to provide the most comfortable home environment for your companion as you both move through stressful times. You have vastly increased your knowledge about nutrition and cancer. Remember, your dog is your partner, friend, and companion. You are the love of their life. No one can ever provide such an exchange of faithfulness and devotion in life as you and your dog share. Your dog knows they are loved.

Afterword
Toward A Standard of
Nutritional Intervention

Our purpose in writing this book was to develop and recommend a nutrition regimen to be used as standard practice by pet owners and veterinarians to prevent and treat cancer in dogs. While nutritional intervention has been recognized by some experts as an effective tool in the fight against cancer in dogs for the past 30 plus years due the work of Gregory Ogilvie, many dog owners and veterinarians are unaware or unwilling to use this tool. This is not just an issue with dogs, but with people as well even though there is more awareness that people eating the right types of foods are less likely to get sick. While there are a number of books on the market now touting the benefits of nutrition as it relates to cancer, we believe that our book will help to make a nutrition regimen part of the treatment plan for as many dogs as possible.

Our NR Plan establishes nutritional programs between pet owners and veterinarians. A practical approach provides easily understood alternatives for the best pet care owners can give to their beloved companions. A diet can be tailored to fit the individual needs of the dog.

Our NR Process facilitates communication and promotes nutritional values. It entails actions for dog owners to collaborate with veterinarians to develop a prescribed course of treatment and diet for promotion of health.

Our NR Steps establish principles for health and nutrition for dog owners and veterinarians. Goals may be designed for integrating diet, feeding and weight control. NR Steps facilitate the process for positive change for dog owners with veterinarians for diet management.

Our NR Diet is based on starving cancer cells of any energy sources while essential nutrients are provided for dogs with cancer. The regimen diet focuses on decreasing inflammation and strengthening the immune system.

Our NR Menu provides ideas for planning and preparing appetizing nutritional meals. The regimen diet provides the right nourishment for your dog, not the cancer. Food and nutrition can be your most valuable allies. You can slow the growth of cancer and strengthen your dog. By anticipating the negative nutritional impacts of cancer and cancer treatments, you can adjust your dog's nutrient profile and potentially avoid some of the side effects. Take charge of your dog's nutritional needs for cancer management to increase your dog's quality of life and survival time.

Cited Works

AAHA (2019). *6 Most Common Canine Cancers.* https://www.aaha. org/pet_owner/lifestyle/6-most-common-canine-cancers.aspx

American Kennel Club Canine Health Foundation (2009). *Canine Lymphoma.* www.akddhf,org/canine-health/your-dogs-health/ canine-lymphoma.html

Ball, L. (2013). *When Your Dog Has Cancer – Making the Right Decisions for You and Your Dog.* Wenatchee, WA: Dogwise Publishing.

Banfield Pet Hospital. (2012). Essential Nutrients For Dogs and Cats: Vitamins. https://www.banfield.com/pet-healthcare/additional-resources/article-

Barber, E. (2018). *Vitamin B-12 and Dogs: Is Your Dog Deficient?* https://www.animalbiome.com/blog/b12-deficiency-in-dogs-and-the-role-of-the-gut

Basko, I. (2018). *Medicinal Mushrooms for Dogs: Multi-Dimensional Healing.* https://www.dogsnaturallymagazine.com/medicinal-mushrooms-for-dogs-multi-dimensional-healing/

Bauhaus, J. (2019). Dangers of Raw Diets for Dogs. *Hill's.* https:// www.hillspet.com/dog-care/nutrition-feeding/dangers-of-raw-diets-for-dogs

Becker, K. (2018). *Why Do Some Dogs Get Cancer More Than Others.* http://healthypets.mercola.com/sites/healthypets/ archive/2016/05/18/goldenretriever-cancer.aspx

Berns, G. (2013). *How Dogs Love Us: A Neuroscientist and His Adopted Dog Decode the Brain.* Boston: Houghton Mifflin Harcourt.

Billinghurst, I. (2016). *Pointing the Bone at Cancer.* Bathurst, Australia: Warrigal Publishing.

Blarnodottir, M. (2018). The 56 Most Common Names for Sugar. *Nutrition.* https://www.healthline.com/nutrition/56/different-names-for-sugar

Blaylock, R. (2010). *The Natural Vet's Guide to Preventing and Treating Cancer in Dogs.* In S. Messennier. (p. viii). Novata, CA: New World Library.

Brown, D. & Reetz, J. (2012). Single Agent Polysaccharopeptide Delays Metastases and Improves Survival in Naturally Occurring Hemangiosarcoma. *Evidence and Complementary and Alternative Medicine.* Pub Med (5):384301 Doi: 10.1155/2012/384306

Brunty, M. (2020). *Chaga: Why This Fungus is Good For Your Dog.* https://www.dogsnaturallymagazine.com

Bullyade (2020). Riboflavin/bullyade.com/riboflavin-vitamin-b2-how-it-affects-your-dogs-health/

Burns, M. (2019). The Latest in Treating Canine Lymphoma. *Veterinary Practice News.* https://www.veterinarypracticenews.com/the-latest-in-treating-canine-lymphoma/

Cancer Veterinary Centers (2019). *Top 5 Cancers in Dogs.* http://www.Cancervetsfl.com/top-5-cancers-dogs/

Cleveland Clinic (2019). *Omega-3 Fatty Acids.* https://my.clevelandclinic.org/health/articles/17290-omega-3-fatty-acids

Chilkov, N. (2017). *Six Cancer-Fighting Medicinal Mushrooms.* IntegrativeCancerAnswers.com

Chun, R. (2009). Lymphoma: Which Chemotherapy Protocol and Why? *Topics in Companion Animal Medicine,* 24, (3), 157-162. Elsevier Inc.

Coates, J. (2019). 9 Dog Breeds Prone to Cancer. National Canine Cancer Foundation.Pet MD.

Courchaine, J. (2019). *5 Trace Minerals Your Dog Needs in His Diet.* https:www.dogsnaturallymagazine.com/5-trace-minerals-your-dog-needs-in-his-diet/.

Couto, C. (2013). Lymphoma in the Dog: COP, CHOP, or Something Else? *Oncology. American Animal Hospital Association*, 379-383.

Danks, L. (2014). The Roles of Calcium and Phosphorus. https://veterinary-practice.com/article/the-roles-of-calcium-and-phosphorus

Dobbins, B. (2020). Studies have Linked Lawn Pesticides with Canine Malignancy. *Whole Dog Journal.* Belvoir Media Group.

Dodds, W. and Laverdure, D. (2015). *Canine Nutrigenomics. The New Science of Feeding Your Dog for Optimum Health*. Wenatchee, WA: Dogwise Publishing.

Dodds, W. (2013). The Canine Immune System and Disease Resistance. http://www.canine-epilepsy-guardian-angels.com/Immune-System.htm

Dow, S. (2020). A Role for Dogs in Advancing Cancer Immunotherapy Research. http://www.frontiersin.org/articles/10.3389/fimmu.2019.02935/full

Downing, R. (2018). Feeding the Canine Patient. http://vcahospitals.com/know-your-pet/feeding-the-canine-patient

Drake, M. (2019). Drake Center for Veterinary Care. https://www.thedrakecenter.com/services/dogs/dog-cancer

Drake, M. (2019). Drake Center for Veterinary Care. https://www.thedrakecenter.com/services/dogs/dog-cancer

Dressler, D. (2011). *The Dog Cancer Survival Guide*. Maui Media LLC.

Eldredge, D. and Bonham, M. (2005). *Cancer and Your Pet: The Complete Guide to the Latest Research*. Sterling, VA: Capital Books, Inc.

Fine, K. (2018). How to Cope with a Serious Diagnosis. http://thebark.com/content/10-tips-navigating-tough-decisions-about-your-dog.

Fox, J. (2020). Understanding the Science Behind Pet food Palatability. https://digital.petfoodprocessing.net/soslandlpdf2019-03-01/index.php#/14

Freitas, D. & Campos, M. (2019). Protective Effects of Omega-3 Fatty Acids in Cancer-Related Complications. Nutrients. https://www.ncbi.nim.nih.gov/pmc/articles/PMC6566772/

Freeman, K. & Ulbrich, B. (2019). *Canine Lymphoma Causes.* https://caninelymphoma.com/canine-lymphoma-causes/

Freeman, K. & & Ulbrich, B. (2019). *Canine Lymphoma Stages.* https://caninelymphoma.com/canine-lymphoma-stages/

Freeman, K. & Ulbrich, B. (2019). *Canine Lymphoma Chemotherapy Madison Wisconsin Protocol.* https://caninelymphoma.com/caninelymphoma-chemotherapy-madison-

Freeman, K., Linder, D., & Heinze, C. (2017). Feeding Pets with Cancer. *Pets With Health Conditions, Trending Topics in Pet Nutrition.* https://vetnutrition.tufts.edu/2017/08/cancer_diet/

Freeman, L. (2012). Cachexia and Sarcopenia: Emerging Syndromes of Importance in Dogs and Cats. *Journal of Veterinary Medicine.* https://doi.org/10.1111/j1939-1676.2011.o8.38x

Fuss, L. (2019). Wasting Away Canine Cachexia. *Cattle Dogs.* http://cattletoday.biz/Wasting-Away-Canine-Cachexia.php

Garcia, J. (2013). Omega-3 Fatty Acids: How Much is Too Much. Medicine? Medicine Center. http://veterinarymedicine.dvm360.com/journal

Gavin, V. and Walle, M. (2019). What Are Simple Sugars? Simple Carbohydrates Explained. *Nutrition.* https://www.healthline.com/nutrition/simple-sugars

Gear, E. (2020). *All About Vitamin Supplements for Dogs and When to Use Them.* Rover.com, The Dog People

Geier, E. (2018). 8 Early Warning Signs of Canine Cancer that Dog Owners Can't Ignore. *Rover.com.* http://www.rover.com/blog/8-early warning-signs-canine-cancer-dog-owners-need-know/).

Govier, R. (2019). Special Diets for Dogs with Cancer. *Whole Dog Journal.* https://www.whole-dog-journal./com/health/special-diets-dogs-with-cancer/

GroCycle (2019). *Medicinal Mushroom Extracts and Supplements: A Buyers Guide.* https://grocycle.com/mushroom-extracts-and-supplements

Halse, H. (2019). Common Foods Containing Simple Sugars You Might Want to Limit. https://www.livestrong.com/article/246693-list-of-foods-that-contain-simple-sugars/

Harper, A. (1958). Balance and imbalance of amino acids. *Annals of the New York Academy of Sciences*, 69, 1025-1041. https://nyaspubs.onlinelibrary.wiley.com/doi/abs/10.1111/j.1749-

Harper, S. (2019). Safer Flea and Tick Treatments for Dogs. *Dog Cancer Blog*, August 19, 2019.

Holland, C. (2018). Anti-Cancer Diets for Dogs. *Whole Dog Journal.* https://www.whole-dog-journal.com//issues6_11/features/Anti-Cancer-Diets-For

Hunter, T. & Downing, R. (2019). *Palliative Care for Dogs.* https://vcahospitals.com/know-your-pet/palliative-care

Jacobson, M. (2018). How to Make Decisions about Dog Cancer Treatments. Dog Cancer.

Jennings, K. (2019). Why Shiitake Mushrooms Are Good For You. *Healthline.*

Jordon, P. (2020). Probiotics for Dogs: A Vet's Perspective. https://www.dogsnaturallymagazine.com/6-best---probiotics-for-dogs/

Jung, A. (2019). *12 Warning Signs of Cancer in Dogs That Every Owner Should Know.* PETS http://www.rd.com/advice/pets/dogs-cancer-signs/

Jung, H., Kang, B., Cho, K., Jeon, J., Lee, H., Moon, J., Jang, H., Kim, J., Jung, D. (2012). Response Rates and Survival Times for Dogs with Lymphoma Treated with the University of Wisconsin-Madison Chemotherapy Protocol. *FutureTech*, 2, 129-133.

Kaneene, J. & Miller, R. (1999). Re-analysis of 2,4-Duse and the occurrence of canine malignant lymphoma. *Veterinary and Human Toxicology*, 41(3), p. 164-170.

Klingemann, H. (2019). The Race to Develop Immunotherapies for Canine Lymphoma and Osteosarcoma. *Veterinary Practice News*. https://www.veterinarypracticenews.com/oncoimmunology-january-2019/

Klingemann, H. (2018). Immunotherapy for Dogs: Running behind Humans. *Frontiers in Immunology*, 9, 133.

Kritikos, G., Parr, J., & Verbrugghe, A., (2017). The role of Thiamine and Effects of Deficiency in Dogs and Cats. *Veterinary Science*, Dec 4(4), 59.

Kubala, W. (2018). 5 *Immune-Boosting Benefits of Turkey Tail Mushroom*. Healthline. https://www.healthline.com/nutrition/turkey-tail-mushroom

Learning Library (2013). Protein Contents of Foods. *Today's Dietitian*.

Lehman, A. (2017). *Use Maitake Mushroom to Complement Dog Immune Systems*. https://pettao.com/use-maitake-mushroom-complement-dog-immune-system/

Lee, E. (2019). Raw Dog Food: Dietary Concerns, Benefits, and Risks. https://pets.webmd.com/dogs/guide/raw-dog-food-dietary-concerns-benefits-and-risks#1

Lenox, C. (2021). Role of Dietary Fatty Acids in Dogs and Cats. *Today's Veterinary Practice. ACVN Nutrition Notes*. Current Issue.

Lenox, C. & Bauer, J. (2013). Potential Adverse Effects of Omega-3 Fatty Acids in Dogs and Cats. *Journal of Veterinary Internal Medicine*. 27:217-226.

Lewellen, H. (2016). Boosting Tranquility Through Nutrition. http://veterinarymedicine.dvm360.com/boosting-tranquility-through-nutrition

Life Extension Report (2002). Arginine and Fish Oil May Help Cancer Patients Undergoing Chemotherapy. *Life Extension Magazine*. www.lef.org/magazine/mag2002/jul2002_report_arginine_01.htm

Llera, R. & Yuill, C. (2019). Nutrition – General Feeding Guidelines for Dogs. https://vcahospitals.com/know-your-pet/nutrition

Lori, J., Stein, T. & Thamm, D. (2010). Doxorubicin and Cyclophosphamide for the Treatment of Canine Lymphoma: A Randomized, Placebo-Controlled Study. *Vet Comp Oncol* 8(3), 188-195.

Lyles, S. (2013). Lymphoma in Dogs. *MEDVET. Medical and Cancer Centers for Pets.*

MacDonald, V. (2009). Chemotherapy: Managing side effects and safe handling. *Can Vet Journal*, 50, 665-668.

Marian, M. & August, D. (2014). Prevalence of Malnutrition & Current Use of Nutrition Support in Current Patients. *Journal Parenter Enteral Nutr*, 38(2): 163-165.

Marssden, S., Messonnier, S. & Yuill, C., (2009). *Fish Oil*. Lifelearn, Inc. http://vcahospitals.com/know-your-pet/fish-oil

McGowan, R. (2016). "Oiling the Brain" or "Cultivating the Gut": Impact of Diet on Anxious Behavior in Dogs. Nestle Purina Companion Animal Nutrition Summit. *Proceedings*, 87-93.

Messonnier, S. (2006). *The Natural Vet's Guide to Preventing and Treating Cancer in Dogs.* Novato, CA: New World Library.

Mitchener K. & Ogilvie, G. (2002). Understanding compassion fatigue: keys for the caring veterinary healthcare team. *Journal of the American Animal Hospital Association*, 38,(4) 307-10

Modiano, J. (2009). *Canine Lymphoma*. Retrieved from http://www.akcchf.org/canine-health/your-dogs-health/canine-lymphoma.html

Moore, A. (2007) *What is the best protocol for Canine Lymphoma.* Proceedings of the World Small Animal Veterinary Association. Sydney, Australia.

National Academy of Sciences (2006). Your Dog's Nutritional Needs. A Science-Based Guide for Pet Owners. Washington, D.C.: The National Academic Press.

National Animal Supplement Council (2019). *Thiamine Deficiency in Dogs.* https://nasc.cc/pet-university/thaimine-deficiency-dogs/

National Canine Cancer Foundation (2018). *Lymphoma.* https://wearthecure.org

National Institutes of Health (2019). *Selenium Fact Sheet for Professionals.* https://ods.od.nih.gov/factsheets/seleium,

National Research Council (2006). *Fats and Fatty Acids. Nutrition Requirements of Dogs and Cats.* Washington D.C.: The National Academic Press, pp 86-110.

Natural Dog Health (2019). *Selenium Benefits to Dogs.* https://www.natural-dog-health-remedies.com/selenium-benefits-.html

Nutrition for the Canine Patient (2000). CanineCancer.com http://www.caninecancer.com/nutrition.html

Nutrition and Cancer (2018). *Expert Nutritional Advice and Helping Your Dog's Cancer.* https: www.health-for-dogs.com/articles/expert-nutritional-advice-helping-your-dogs-cancer.

Ogilvie, G. (2006). Amazing Advances in Veterinary Oncology Today. *Veterinarian Forum.* July, 39-46.

Ogilvie, G. & Moore, A. (2006). Cancer Cachexia as a Manifestation of Malignancy. *Standards of Care Emergency and Critical Care Medicine. Adapted from Managing the Canine Cancer Patient: A Practical Guide to Compassionate Care.* Yardley, PA: Veterinary Learning Systems, p. 320-322.

Ogilvie, G. (2004). *Canine Lymphoma: Protocols For 2004.* http://www.vin.com/Proceedings/.plxCID=WSAVA2004&PID=8710&O=Generic

Ogilvie, G. (2002). *Proceedings from WSAVA Congress, Nutrition and Cancer: Exciting Advances for 2002.* http://www.vin.com/Proceedings.plx?CID=WSAVA2002&PID=2638

Ogilvie, G. (2001). Metabolic Alterations and Nutritional Therapy. In Withrow, S., & MacEwen, E.(eds). *Small Animal Clinical Oncology.* Philidelphia, PA:W.B. Saunders Co.

Ogilvie, G., Fettman, M., Mallinckrodt, C., Walton, J., Hansen, R., Davenport, D., Gross, K., Richardson, K., Rogers, Q., & Hand, M. (2000). Effect of Fish Oil, Arginine, and Doxorubicin. Chemotherapy on Remission and Survival Time for Dogs with Lymphoma. *Cancer,* 88, 1916-28.

Ogilvie, G. (1999). Nutritional approaches to Cancer Therapy. In Schoen, A. & Winn, S. (Eds.), *Complementary and Alternative Veterinary Medicine*. St. Louis: Mosby Press.

Ogilvie, G. (1998). New Hope For Pet Cancer Victims. http://www.cbsnews.com/2100-870_162-8433html

Ogilvie, A. & Moore, A. (1995). Managing The Veterinary Cancer Patient. Yardley, PA: MediMedia.

Ogilvie, G., Davenport, D., Gross, K. & Hand, M. (1995). *Therapeutic Diet for Metabolic Abnormalities Found in Animals with Lymphoma*. Google Patents, US577691A.

Olsen, N. (2018). Twenty foods rich in Selenium. *Healthline*. Healthline Media.

Olson, L. (1998). *Nutrition for Dogs with Cancer*. http.//www.naturals.com/newsletter/nutrition-for-dogs-with-cancer/

Pask, E. & Scott, L. (2018). The Cancer Diet for Dogs. *Modern Dogs Magazine*. http://moderndogmagzine.com/articles/cancer-Diet-dogs/19669.

Petary, K. (2019). Helping Dogs and Humans with Cancer: NCI's Comparative Oncology Studies. National Cancer Institute.

PetCure Oncology. *Which Pet Cancer Treatment Option is Right for You*. https://petcureoncology.com/making-a-treatment-decision/treatments/

Pletcher, J. (2018). Which Foods Are High In Arginine? *Medical New Today*. https://www.medicalnewstoday.com/articles/323259.php

Richter, G. (2017). *The Ultimate Pet Health Guide: Break Through Nutrition and Integrative Care for Dogs and Cats*. New York: Hay House Publishing.

Saker, K. (2014). Practical Approaches to Feeding the Cancer Patient. *Today's Veterinary Practice*. https://todaysveterinarypractice.com/acvn-nutrition-notes-practical-approaches-to-feeding-the-cancer-patient/

Saker, K., & Selting, K. (2010). Cancer. Edited by Hand, M., Thatcher, C., Roudebush, P., et al (eds). *Small Animal Clinical Nutrition*, 5th ed. Topeka, KS: Mark Morris Institute. Pp 587-607.

Scott, D. (2019). *Medicinal Mushrooms for Cancer in Dogs.* https://www.dogsnaturallymagazine.com/medicinal-mushrooms-for-cancer-in-dogs/

Scott Endowed Program in Veterinary Oncology. (2013). *Cancer Therapies.* http://www.cvm.missouri.edu/oncology/therapies.html

Seafood Health Facts: Making Smart Choices. Balancing the Benefits and Risks of Seafood Consumption. *Resources for Healthcare Providers.* http://www.seafoodhealthfcts.org/seafood-nutrition/healthcare-professionals/omega-3-

Sean, R. (2018). *Top 5 Mushrooms for Fighting Cancer in Dogs*: DoggieHerbs. https://www.dogherbs.com/top -5-best-musshrooms-fighting-cancer-dogs/

Selamwit, A. & Klingemann, H. (2018). Cellular Immunotherapy of Canine Cancer. *Veterinarian Science* 5(4):100.

Self-Nutrition Data, Know What You Eat (2019). Foods High in Arginine. *Self.* https://nutritiondata.self.com/foods

Selting, K. (2019). *Radiation Makes Cancer Cells Unable to Reproduce.* http://vetmed.illinois.edu/pet-column/radiation-therapy

Selting, K., Ogilvie G., Gustafson, D., et al., (2006), Evaluation of the effects of dietary n-3fatty acid supplementation on the pharmacokinetics of doxorubicin in dogs with lymphoma. *American Journal Veterinary Research*, 67, 145-51.

Smarter Reviews. *Omega-3 Fish Oil Guide.* https://smarter-reviews.com/lp/sr-omega3

Spielman, B. (2015). *Structure and Function of the Lymphatic System in Dogs.* http://www.petplace.com/article/dogs/pet-health/structure-and-function-of-the-lymphatic-system-in-dogs-

Sharadamma, K. (2011). Role of Selenium in Pets Health and Nutrition: A Review. *Asian Journal of Animal Sciences.* Vol 5(1): 64-70.

Straus, M. (2018). Improve Your Dog's Digestion with Digestive Enzyme Supplements. *Whole Dog Journal.* https://www.whole-dog-journal.com/health/digestion-with-digestive-enzyme-supplements/

Stubbs, R. & Blundell, J. (2013). Palatability: An Overview. *Encyclopedia of Human Science. Meat Science.*

Tinggi, U. (2008). Selenium: Its Role as Antioxidant in Human Health. *Environmental Health Prev Med.* March, 13(2): 102-108.

Tollett, M., Duda, L. & Brown, D. (2016). Palliative Radiation Therapy for Solid Tumors in Dogs. *Journal of American Veterinary Medical Association,* Jan, (248), 72-82.

Tudor, K. (2013). Fish Oil: The Dangers of Too Much. https://www.petmd.com/blogs/thedailyvet/ktudo/2013/aug/the-dangers-of-too-much-

USDA National Nutrient Database for Standard Reference. (2019). http://www.nal.usda.gov/fnic/foodcomp/search/

Vail, D., Ogilvie, G., and Wheeler, S. (1990). Metabolic Alterations in Patients with Cancer Cachexia. *Compendium on Continuing Education for the Practice Veterinarian* 12: 381-7.

Valli, V., Kass, P., San Myint, M., & Scott, F. (2013). Canine Lymphomas: Association of Classification Type, Disease Stage, Tumor Subtype, Mitotic Rate, and Treatment With Survival. *Vet Pathology* 50(5):738-48.

Vey, E. (2020). *Biotin for Dogs: Is Deficiency a Risk.* https://www.dognaturallymagazine.com/biotin-for-dogs-is-deficiency-a-risk-for-your-dog/

Volhard, W. & Brown, K. (2000). The Cancer Diet. In *The Holistic Guide for a Healthy Dog.* Howell Book House.

Wall, T. (2018). Fatty Acids, Vitamin Supplements May Help Dog Behavior. Watt Global Media. http://www.wattglobalmedia.com

Ward, E. (2017). *Beyond the Belly: The Health Consequences of Pet Obesity.* Veterinary Practice News. https://www.veterinarypracticenews.com/beyond-the-belly-the-health-consequences-of-pet-obesity/

Weeth, L. (2008). *Fat Facts on Cancer: Obesity & Cancer Preva-lence.* https://www.vin.com/apputil/content/defaultadv1. aspx?id=3865426&pid

Whitechurch, D. (2019). *What You Need to Know Before Buying any Medicinal Mushroom Supplement.* https://teelixir.com/blogs/news/ what-you-need-to-know-

Williams, K. & Downing, R. (2019). *Obesity in Dogs.* https://vca-hospitals.com//know-your-pet/obesity-in-dogs

Wilson-Robles, H. (2013). *Second–hand Smoke and Your Pet.* http:// vetmed.tamu.edu/news/pet/talk/second-hand-smoke-and-your-pet.

Winn, S. (2013). *Total Cancer Management of Small Animals.* www. uvma.org/cancer.htm

Wittich, M. (2019). Omega-3 For dogs: What is it? Benefits, Sources and Dosage. *Campfire.* https://campfiretreats.com/blogs/campfire-tales/omega-3-for-dogs

World Health Organization (2008). *World Cancer Report.* IARC Press. Lyon, France.

Yin, S. (2017). Do Environmental Pollutants Cause Cancer in Dogs? *The Bark.* 44: Sept-Oct.

Zeltzman, P. (2018). 10 Signs of Cancer in Dogs. *Dog Health.* IDEXX.Laboratories, Inc. http://www.perhealthnetwork.com/dog-health/dog-diseases-conditions-a-z/10-signs-cancer-

Glossary

Alternative medicine – Non-conventional cancer therapy using natural healing mechanisms of the body in a whole or total body approach.

Amino acids – The building blocks of protein.

Anemia – A condition marked by decreased red blood cells resulting in weakness.

Antibodies – A protein produced by the body's immune system when it detects a foreign or harmful substance.

Antioxidant – A substance that reduces damage caused by free radicals created during oxidation.

Anorexia – Loss or lack of appetite for food.

Arginine – An amino acid used in the biosynthesis of protein, commonly found in foods like leaf or chopped spinach, turkey, eggs, pork roast, cooked or canned tuna, and oven roasted chicken breast.

Bacteria – Single-celled microscopic organisms not visible to the naked eye, some of which cause disease.

Beta-glucans – Types of fiber found in yeast, algae, fungi and bacteria. They are also found in oats, barley and certain types of mushrooms. Immune system boosters.

Bioavailable – The ability of a drug or other substance to be absorbed and used by the body.

Biotin – Type of vitamin B necessary for fat, protein, and carbohydrate utilization by body.

Cachexia – Complex syndrome affecting many dogs with cancer, characterized by loss of lean body mass and involuntary loss of body weight.

Carbohydrates – Sugars, starches, and fibers found in fruits, grains, vegetables, and milk products.

CHOP combination therapy – Cancer treatment combining three chemotherapy drugs, Vincristine, Doxorubicin, and Cytoxan.

Choline – Basic compound occurring in living tissues important in synthesis and transport of lipids.

Cobalamin – Also called vitamin B-12, needed for red blood cell development and important in preventing anemia.

Complementary medicine – Term used for nonconventional cancer treatment using the natural healing mechanisms of the body.

Dog-friendly carbohydrates – Carbohydrates including spinach, broccoli, carrots, Brussels sprouts, and cauliflower.

Du jour – The menu changes daily, depending on what is available from chef.

Enzyme – A substance in living organisms that regulates the rate of chemical reactions without being altered itself in the process.

Fat – A type of nutrient that gives energy and absorbs vitamins.

Food aversion – When a former favorite food becomes one causing nausea or an unpleasant taste.

Folic acid – Also called vitamin B-9, it is needed for formation of healthy red blood cells and important for reproduction.

Free radicals – Unstable molecules made by the process of oxidation during normal metabolism. Free radicals may play a part in cancer.

Glutamine – Essential amino acid in dogs preferred by the mucous lining of the digestive tract for rebuilding tissues damaged by vomiting or diarrhea from cancer or treatments.

Hemangiosarcoma – Highly malignant cancer arising from cells lining blood vessels of various tissues of the body.

Homeostatic balance – Ability to maintain a relative stable internal environment.

Immune system – The body's system responsible for maintaining the dog's resistance to disease.

Immunotherapy – Treatment using the body's natural defenses to fight cancer.

Lactate – Waste product produced by cells as the body turns food into energy, becoming a poison stealing energy for dogs with cancer.

Lethargy – Sluggish, fatigued, or inactive behaviors.

Lipid – Class of organic compounds that are fatty acids and are insoluble in water.

Lymphoma – A common type of cancer in dogs appearing in the white blood cells, lymph nodes, bone marrow, spleen, liver, and gastrointestinal tract. It is the most treatable of all types of cancer, but not curable.

Mammary cancer – A type of cancer commonly found in female dogs that were not spayed.

Manganese – Trace mineral necessary for bone growth and quality of cartilage.

Mast cell tumors – A common type of cancer found in skin, intestines, respiratory tract, and other tissues.

Medicinal mushrooms – Considered a miracle plant containing medicinal properties for natural healing to fight cancer and enhance the immune system.

Melanoma – The most common malignant cancer.

Metabolism – Chemical reactions within a living organism in order to maintain life.

Metastasis – When cancer spreads from a body area where it started to different areas of the body.

Monosaccharides – The simplest form of sugar and most basic unit of carbohydrates. Glucose and fructose are examples of monosaccharides.

Neuromuscular transmission – A process that allows the central nervous system to control the movement of muscles.

Niacin – Also known as vitamin B-3, it promotes appetite and aids in the digestive process.

Nutrition Regiment Diet – High amounts of omega-3 fatty acids from food sources or supplements comprised of 37% animal protein, 32% fat mostly from animal sources and 20% dog friendly carbohydrates.

Nutrition Regimen Menu – Ideas for planning and preparing appetizing and nutritional meals. The type of menu is De jour, meaning the menu may change daily with special chef preparations.

Nutrition Regimen Plan – A scheme for integrating diet, feeding, and weight management for or meeting health and treatment needs of dogs with cancer.

Nutrition Regimen Process – Actions to communicate and promote nutritional values by owners and veterinarians for a prescribed course of treatment and diet for promotion of health of dogs with cancer.

Nutrition Regimen Steps – Procedures or measures for dog owners and veterinarians to follow to develop as an ultimate nutrition treatment program. Goals may be designed for integrating diet, feeding and weight management.

Obesity – Accumulation of body fat causing a chronic, low-level inflammatory condition that is totality preventable by dog owners. The dog's energy intake exceeds energy demand and overweight/ obesity are the result.

Omega-3 fatty acids – Fish oil or essential fatty acids providing a source of energy that can not be synthesized in the dog's body and must be supplied through foods.

Osteosarcoma – A type of bone cancer.

Palatability – Capacity of food or an ingredient to stimulate appetite.

Pantothenic acid – Also known as vitamin B-5, it is used for treating stress, anxiety, and depression.

Probiotic – Live organisms, known as good bacteria, in the dog's body.

Protein – A macronutrient that is essential to building muscle mass.

Protein synthesis – Process of building muscle mass.

Pyridoxine – Also known as vitamin B-6, it facilitates glucose generation and formation of red blood cells.

Radiation therapy – A localized treatment to achieve tumor control.

Regimen – Prescribed course of medical treatment and specific diet plan designed to improve, maintain, and preserve health. It is a structured process and diet plan designed for the restoration of health.

Remission – When signs and symptoms of cancer have completely or partially disappeared in response to cancer treatment.

Riboflavin – Also called vitamin B-2, it is necessary for cell physiology and cell metabolism.

Seizure – Uncontrolled, strong, jerking motions or chewing of paws and foaming at the mouth.

Selenium – A trace mineral and powerful antioxidant.

Satiety – Feeling of fullness and suppression of hunger for period of time after a meal.

Symbiotic – Mutually beneficial interaction between two different organisms living in close physical association.

The Standard of Nutritional Intervention – A quality, science-based nutrition program for dogs with cancer (Nutrition Regimen) presenting a plan, process, steps, diet, and menu.

Thiamine – Also known as vitamin B-1, it promotes good appetite, regulates energy, and activates functions of the nervous system.

Urea Cycle – The urea cycle is the metabolic pathway that transforms nitrogen to urea for excretion from the body.

Appendix
Dog Food Recipe Books

Gallagher, C. (2021). *Pup-Approved Dog Treat Recipes: 80 Homemade Goodies from Paddington's Pantry.*

Jefferson, L. (2017). *Cooking for Dogs-Easy, All-Natural Meal and Treat Recipes for Dogs of All Ages.*

McGraw, C. (2017). *Dog Food Homemade. The Best Nutrition for Your Four Legged Friend.*

Shanahan, S. (2020). *Easy Dog Food Recipes: 60 Healthy Dishes to Feed Your Pet Safely.*

The Woof Brothers (2019). *Dog Nutrition and Cookbook. The Simple Guide to Keeping Your Dog Happy and Healthy.*

Waterson, A. (2019). *Woof! Woof! Best Dog Food Recipes. A Cookbook of Healthy Homemade Foods for Fido.*

About the Authors

Jo Cowden, PhD

Dr. Cowden was professor of motor development and pediatric adapted physical activity at the University of New Orleans for more than 25 years. She served on the editorial board of the Adapted Physical Activity Quarterly from 1997 to 2005. As research professor, she wrote several books, but not related to cancer in dogs. Publications include: *Pediatric Adapted Motor Development and Exercise* (1998), *Motor Development and Movement Activities for Preschools and Infants with Delays* (2007) and *The Cowden Pre-autism Observation Inventory* (2011). Her background and experience in academia and from writing prior books provides her the research expertise to compile this book.

Across years, her dogs were the love of her life. She always had a rescue dog as her friend, companion, and family. They traveled with her, hiked with her, studied with her, and lived with her as family. Her dogs had long healthy lives—16 to 18 years of age. To have her beloved American Eskimo dog Addie Kara diagnosed with lymphoma was devastating. Chemotherapy treatments were administered; however, she learned that she could contribute to Addie's recovery by providing her with a specialized nutrition program. As an advocate for nutritional intervention, Dr. Cowden has developed a scheme for integrating diet, feeding and weight management for meeting health and treatment needs of dogs with cancer.

Using her research expertise, she turned to the Internet to find confusing and conflicting information. She reviewed books and peer-reviewed journals on nutrition for dogs with cancer. Her goal was to compile an accurate and comprehensive book for those who would experience the same overwhelming diagnosis of lymphoma for their dog. Dr. Cowden has written this book for you— so you with your veterinarian— can provide your dog with an alternative for care, a prescribed course for nutrition treatment and specific diet plan. She wants you to feel confident and empowered to make the best decisions with your veterinarian for nutrition intervention.

Dr. Cowden lives in River Ridge, Louisiana, with her rescue Siberian Husky, Luna Blue. They spend their time on long walks on the Mississippi levee and in the beautiful parks of New Orleans.

Dr. Connie McMillan, DVM

Dr. Connie McMillan was raised in the New Orleans area and attended Louisiana State University School of Veterinary Medicine. She has always wanted to be a veterinarian, but her life took a different course. After years in the printing industry, she decided it was time to pursue her dream and return to school. Veterinary Medicine is her second career, and she is thrilled to finally be living her dream of working with animals.

Dr. McMillan graduated with a Doctorate in Veterinary Medicine in 2008. She completed a Medical and Surgical Internship at Southeast Veterinary Specialists before joining the VCA team in Metairie. She is now Medical Director of the Airline location. Dr. McMillan continues to practice at VCA Airline Animal Hospital.

She lives in Harahan, Louisiana, with her three dogs: Grits, a deaf Staffordshire Bull Terrier, and Clementine and Elodie, mixed, rescue dogs.

A

alternative medicine, 21
American Cancer Society, 23
American College of Veterinary Nutrition, 24
American Eskimos, iv, vi
amino acids
    arginine, 23–24, 40, 51–54
    changes in metabolism, 10, 32–34
    diet overview, 27–29
    effects on cancer, 4–7
    glutamine, 24, 57–59, 73–74
    in mushrooms, 47
antioxidants
    effects on cachexia, 10
    importance of, 4
    sources, 37, 47–49, 54–56, 64, 71–73
anxiety, 41
arginine
    diet overview, 27–29
    effects on cancer, 23–24, 40, 51–53
    metabolic changes, 33
    overview, 4, 6
    sources, 72–74

B

Banfield Pet Hospital, 60
Basko, I., 48, 49
bathroom habits, 12
B-cells, 14, 16–17
Beagles, 13
behavior patterns, 40–41
beta-glucans, 46, 49
biotin, 62
blood cancers, 18
body weight, 4–5, 12, 15. *See also* cachexia
bone cancer, 18
Boxers, 13
brain cancer, 58
breakfast suggestions, 71–72
breathing changes, 12
breeding factors, 13
Brown, D., 46–47
Brunty, M., 48
bumps, 11

C

cachexia
    dietary considerations, 23–26, 29
    omega-3 fatty acids and, 40, 45
    overview, 5, 9–12
calcium, 47, 63–64, 73
Campos, M., 40
carbohydrates
    changes in metabolism, 9–10, 30–32
    diet overview, 28
    effects on cancer, 5
    overview, 6
causes of cancer, 13–16
Chaga (Inonotus obliquus) mushroom, 48
chemotherapy
    immune system, 14, 25, 40–41
    overview, 18–20
    research, 23
    side effects, 4, 7, 33, 38, 47–48, 57
Chilkov, N., 48
chloride, 64
chlorophylls, 32
choline, 63
Chun, R., 19
cigarettes, 15
cobalamin, 61–62
complementary medicine, 21
copper, 65
Cordyceps mushroom, 48–49
coughing, 11
Couto, C., 19
Cowden, Jo, vi–vii

D

depression, 41
diagnosis of cancer, 11–13
diet overview, 27–29, 34, 36, 43
digestive enzymes supplements, 37
dinner entrees, 73–74
Dobbins, B., 14
Dodds, W., 33, 47
Dressler, D., 40, 57, 60

E

exercise, 78

Also available from Dogwise Publishing

Go to dogwise.com for more books and ebooks

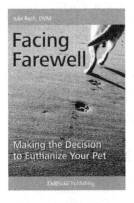

Facing Farewell

MAKING THE DECISION TO EUTHANIZE YOUR PET

Julie Reck, DVM

One of the most difficult aspects of being a pet owner is making end of life decisions for beloved dogs and cats. While many end up deciding to put their pet to sleep, the euthanasia procedure remains a mystery for most people adding to the stress and fear an owner experiences at this critical time.

When Your Dog Has Cancer

MAKING THE RIGHT DECISIONS FOR YOU AND YOUR DOG

Lola Ball

While some dogs diagnosed with cancer can be treated successfully and survive for years, a diagnosis of cancer for your dog often means the time you have left together is limited. The most important first steps are to arm yourself with knowledge about the different types of cancers, medicines, treatment alternatives and prognoses.

Stress in Dogs

LEARN HOW DOGS SHOW STRESS AND WHAT YOU CAN DO TO HELP

Martina Scholz and Clarissa von Reinhardt

Stress in Dogs is the first book to analyze, explain, and help you resolve stress in the lives of our canine companions. Written for both the canine professional as well as concerned dog owners, the information in *Stress in Dogs* can improve the lives of dogs as well as humans with a sound approach to resolving stress-related problems. Available as an eBook only.

Dogwise.com is your source for quality books, ebooks, DVDs, training tools and treats.

We've been selling to the dog fancier for more than 25 years and we carefully screen our products for quality information, safety, durability and FUN! You'll find something for every level of dog enthusiast on our website, www.dogwise.com, or drop by our store in Wenatchee, Washington.

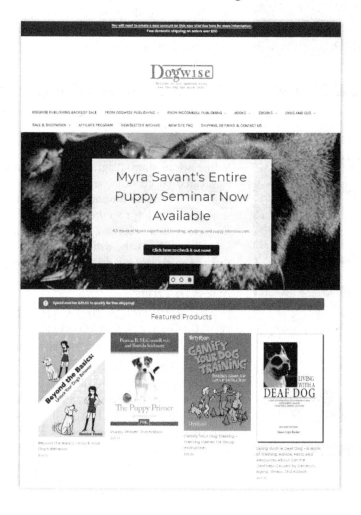

Made in United States
Orlando, FL
16 December 2024

55488359R00065